Creative and Collectible
MINIATURES

by
Lillian Baker

A mini - book with maxi good wishes to Jan Klein ... enjoy!

Lillian Baker

Creative and Collectible
MINIATURES

by
Lillian Baker

Color Photography
by
Dave Hammell

COLLECTOR BOOKS
A Division of Schroeder Publishing Co., Inc.

The current values in this book should be used only as a guide. They are not intended to set prices, which vary from one section of the country to another. Auction prices as well as dealer prices vary greatly and are affected by condition as well as demand. Neither the Author nor the Publisher assumes responsibility for any losses that might be incurred as a result of consulting the values shown in this publication.

Additional copies of this book may be ordered from:

COLLECTOR BOOKS
P.O. Box 3009
Paducah, Kentucky 42001

or

Lillian Baker
15237 Chanera Ave.
Alondra Park, Gardena, California 90249

@ $9.95 plus $1.00 for postage and handling

Copyright: Lillian Baker 1984
ISBN: 0-89145-242-7

Dedication

To My Children,
Wanda & George
and
For My Friend,
"Susie" Hendrix

A SMALL EXPRESSION OF THANKS

The author gratefully acknowledges the participation of the following persons whose variety of miniatures are pictured herein:

Mr. & Mrs. James "Skip" Adair, (Washington)
Mrs. Clare Albert, (Louisiana)
Mrs. Jenny Biddle, Cape Cottage Antiques, (Calif.)
John & Ellen Krucker Blauer, The Miniature Mart, (Calif)
Cecil Boyd, Masterpiece Museum Miniatures, (Texas)
Mrs. Barbara Bunce, (Michigan)
Ms. Stephanie Blythe & Susan Snodgrass, (Maryland)
Mrs. Milly Combs, (California)
Ms. Sue Dennis, (California)
Mr. Gim Fong, (California)
Bonnie & Stephen Goode, (California)
Barbara Lee Hammell, (California)
Mr. & Mrs. Neil Heaslip, (North Carolina)
Ms. Cynthia Herrmann, (California)
Patti & Paul Highfill, (California)
Ms. Miriam Irwin, Mosaic Press, (Ohio)
Mrs. Barbara Kalty, (California)
Mrs. Evelyn De Wolf Nadel, The Gypsy Merchant, (California)
Mr. & Mrs. Roland E. Stieler, (Washington)
Ms. Jinx Lee Theisen, (California)
Mr. Albert G. Thomay, (Florida)
Ms. Georgia Luna Villalobos, (California)

The author fully appreciates the cooperation and talent of photographer Dave Hammell, and his wife Barbara Lee; the complete confidence of her publisher, COLLECTOR BOOKS, and the passive acceptance of her husband so necessary for the completion of this project. Verbal thanks have gone to many in the field who have assisted in various degrees. It would be impossible, within the limited format of this book, to acknowledge all these individual contributions.

ABOUT THE COVER
Vignette by Lillian Baker,
photographed by Dave Hammell.
Description: see *Color Plate 10*

Table of Contents

A LITTLE NOTE TO THE READER

**"...For everything that's lovely is
but a brief, dreamy kind of delight."
(William Butler Yeats, 1865-1939)**

The real minikin world belongs to the mature but young at heart.
Considered unique works of artistic merit, miniatures are not truly
toys. They are fantastic fanciful playthings whose inventiveness and
artistry tax patience, require perseverence, and much bravado! They
are a wagging dalliance that toys with make-believe; they are a dab
for the dilettante, amateur, hobbyist, or recreation-seeker. They can
become the ultimate commentary on ones artistry or endeavor.

This book presents a digest of a diverse art. It will introduce readers
to those who inspire and encourage both novice and professional
miniaturist. The result: one can remain in a happy hobby, or be driven
into a passion for perfection.

For many, minikin-land is an escape to another earth-plane, or an at-
tempt to captivate, clone, and miniaturize the familiar. It is the enjoyment or sheer luxury of losing oneself within ones being without becom-
ing either a social outcast or an introvert.

Indeed, the demands of miniaturing precludes seclusion, for the
greatest dividend and enjoyment is sharing the spell and magic of
miniatures with others.

That's what this book is all about.

Lillian Baker
California

INTRODUCTION
A MINIKIN MYSTERY SOLVED BY A MYTH

"We heard the miniature thunder where he fled."
(The Runaway, **Robert Frost 1874-1963)**

The term *miniature*, whether man-made or of natural origin, evokes reactions of tenderness and fragility. It's therefore not astonishing that first glimpses of miniatures brings warm-heartedness to the human spirit. It brings a contagion of influence upon the viewer akin to amazement; and it beguiles and infects young and old alike.

In the many books written about the subject, none fully trace the history of miniatures to its earliest source. None endeavors to perceive a historical or mythological purpose for composing a counterpart in miniature of everything created by nature or copied by man. What was the early significance of miniaturization? Was it an accomodation to the times when ones worth was bodily adornment or treasures tiny enough to hold in the palm of ones hand?

The author's search for this mysterious source has produced an interesting epoch of a distinct development of miniatures as decorative objects and playthings for adults, as well as showpieces for amusement and bedazzlement.

The 16th, 17th, and 18th centuries excelled in cabinet pieces. These awesome works in precious stones and metals, challenged other masterpieces of artful media. The 19th and 20th centuries contributed even more unique micrified museum pieces, including materials and matter for miniature mansions, scaled to size. Then, with the "machine age", came miniatures "for the masses".

But where, when, and how did it all begin?

Driven by a fervent desire to begin at the beginning, and based on rabid research, the author has concluded that the very first miniature surely depicted that which was closest to both savage and civilized man: God, self, and loved ones.

Prior to orthodox civility, we know that early tribes of many nations carried small fetishes in the palm or hung them on gut-lacings around the neck or waist. When superstitions persisted and invaded cultures, fetishes advanced from mere relics to the more defined objects such as carved gems, gemstones, coinage, and the forefather of all, the *shell* cameo. The latter, it seems would represent the truly first minikin.

Cameos of gem quality are rare and primarily were the jewels of church or nobility. They served as talismans or denoted the wealth or

9

power of the owner. Some cameos of antiquity provide portents for posterity of human and animal habits, of scenes both real and mythological; timeless mirrors of ancestral bygones and yesteryear.

Shell and stone cameos are both being made today, but it is the *miniature portraits* that are still the most highly prized for sentimental, if not monetary, consideration.

But who carved the very first cameo? Did they begin as talismans or tokens of fond remembrance? Although gem miniatures are known since Babylonian times, as is the striking of mini-meter coinage small enough to bank in a drawstring pouch, there's not a single clue as to where or when the shell cameo began as a miniature art form.

Sir Max Beerbohm, in his work "Zuleika Dobson", (1911), referred to the wee but winsome cameo when he scribed: "...she was hardly more affable than a cameo."

Beerbohm's use of the word "affable", when applied to a miniature cameo, added to the quality of intrigue which ensnared the author's imagination within an aura of fantasy. Out of that mystic mood came a figment, a fantasy, a fabrication about the first cameo. And since shells as decorative objects pre-date gems and gemstones as ornaments and barter, it was only natural that this wholly imaginative myth be created about the very first minikin -- the shell cameo. And where else should this tale begin, but the sea. So begins an original "legend" -- *Theola By The Sea* -- first published in the August 16, 1978 edition of *The Antique Trader Weekly*, and included in their *1978 Annual of Articles*. "Cameos: Gems of Intrigue and Imagination" is the title of the author's article which contains the above mentioned myth. The inquisitive reader may obtain a copy by writing: Kyle Husfloen, Editor, *The Antique Trader Weekly*, P.O. Box 1050, Dubuque, Iowa 52001.

Photographs

Plates 1-61

PLATE 1
THE GYPSY MERCHANT'S ANTIQUES SHOPPE was designed and built
by Evelyn De Wolf Nadel, to serve as a showcase from which are sold collectible mini-furnishings for period dollhouses. Steven Paull, a talented young friend
of Mrs. Nadel, helped complete the six month project. All floorboards were individually cut, drilled and pegged; the front steps (not shown), are of genuine
slate. The walkway, comprised of 600 terra-cotta bricks, were individually fired,
then grouted into period design. Potted plants add bright color to this forever
changing operating sales-shop. The shopkeeper, attentive to her prized wares,
has been named "Antoinette", as a loving tribute to Evelyn's mother. "The
Gypsy Merchant's Antiques Shoppe" was "established, 1893," to honor Antoinette's birth-year. All items are for sale, from THE GYPSY MERCHANT,
P.O. Box 2115, Hollywood, CA 90028.
Photo: Leonard Nadel

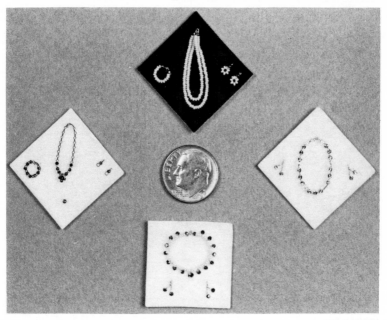

PLATE 2

PLATE 2
Boxed mini-jewelry, each *parure* representing period Victorian, Edwardian, and classic sets of jewels, are meticulously handmade by Barbara Bunce, an extraordinary copier of jewelry in miniature. Choosing uniform beads of microscopic size, is a challenge well-met by this singular technician. (See SOURCES)
Photo: Dave Hammell; Author's Collection

PLATE 3 (Page 14)
Two curio wall cabinets handcrafted by Gim Fong, are displayed at Fong's Los Angeles shop in downtown "Chinatown". Note the United States copper penny shown for scale comparison, with the mini-counterpart in left bottom row. (See SOURCES)
Photo: Dave Hammell; Gim Fong's Collection (Not For Sale)

PLATE 4 (Page 14)
Camphor wood chest, 1-5/8″ high x 2″ deep x 3½″ wide. The handmade brass hardware entailed hours of precision work, and were garnered from old Chinese jewelry findings. The screen insert is carved plastic. Gim Fong copied the chest to 1″-1′ scale, from an all-wood chest in his shop which is a mecca for those who love Orientalia. The Folding Screen, 6″ high, measures 2¼″ wide (3/panels). The inserts were cast from an original carving found in an ivory card holder. Gim Fong carved and constructed the screen, making a rubber mold from the ivory, and then casting it in plaster. (Chest & Screen NFS. Both pieces are displayed in Gim Fong's miniature Oriental Shop. This to-scale shop with its many tiny treasures, is on public display for all to enjoy.)
Photo: Dave Hammell; Gim Fong Collection

PLATE 3

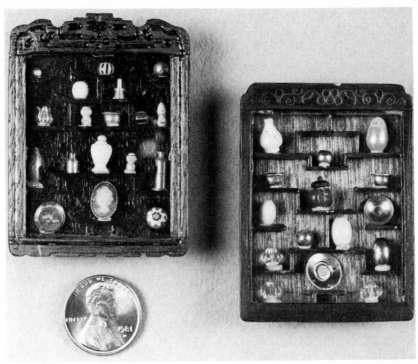

PLATE 4

PLATE 5 AND 6

MINIATURE GLOBE STAND, shown to exact scale on _Plate 5, (below)_ and enlarged to show the attention to exquisite detail, _Plate 6_, (page 16). This 3½" brass Globe Stand is the work of Ellen Krucker Blauer, one of the world's leading miniature craftswomen. Ellen's painstaking attention to detail, countless hours of research, and jeweler-like artistry, is evident in this representative piece of her fine work.

There are many firsts to her credit in the world of miniatures. She was the first to offer miniature wallpaper, which she researched and designed; the first to do a series of authentic Collector's Plates representing some of the most famous patterns from the world's leading china factories. Ellen initiated the first series of miniature Christmas plates, was the first to reproduce in miniature, antique Coca-Cola trays, and is the only person to be granted permission to create the latter by permission of the Coca-Cola Company.

Married to John Blauer, Ellen and John share a common interest in miniatures and have an appreciation of superior craftsmanship and microscopic detail, which they demand of their own creations.

John Blauer has the world's largest collection of perfectly scaled authentically accurate, one inch to the foot miniatures comprising over 8,000 Lilliputian treasures housed in a scaled 42 room structure which bears John's grandmother's maiden name, "Maynard Manor" (ca. 1880).

The Blauer's mail order business, the famous MINIATURE MART, is maintained in a 22 room San Francisco Victorian home, which is also their studio. Seven full-time employees and many artists throughout the world create

miniatures for them and their customers. Every room is dominated by a miniature setting or display case containing their vast collection. The Miniature Mart offers a beautiful catalogue. Since the studio is the Blauer's home, visitors to San Francisco should make an appointment to see this fabulous collection of miniatures on display and for sale. (See SOURCES and CATALOGUES)
Photo: Ellen Krucker Blauer; The Miniature Mart Collection

PLATE 5

PLATE 6

PLATE 7
Musical instruments from the Evelyn DeWolf Nadel collection. Carved fretwork music stand (maker unknown); sterling flute w/ivory mouthpiece by master
craftsman, Geoffrey Bishop. Rosewood & maple Flamenco Guitar, handcrafted
by Bishop, can actually be tuned and played. The Cello, handhewn of spruce,
ebony, and maple, is the work of Joe Greenwood whose specialty is musical
instruments. The Mandolin (foreground), by unknown maker, is inlaid with
mother-of-pearl. All instruments scaled 1":1'. THE GYPSY MERCHANT AN-
TIQUES SHOPPE features unusual one-of-a-kind miniatures. Address queries
to : P.O. Box 2115, Hollywood, CA 90028.
Photo: Leonard Nadel

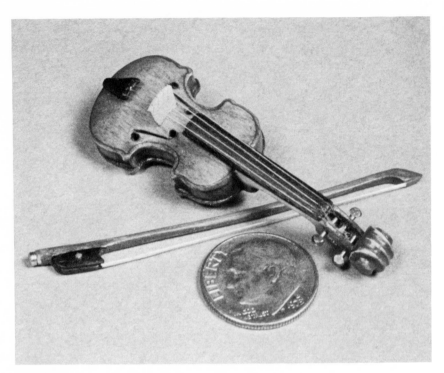

PLATE 8
Marilyn Worth probably crafts the finest miniature violins made anywhere.
The instrument is made of choice cherry and bass woods, using the same prin-
ciples professional luthiers used in olden times to make their fine musical
mediums.

Marilyn began to make violins after vainly searching for one as a gift to her
mother, a great lover of miniature craft. The violins then available, seemed to
her to fill but a "symbolic" need, but none came really close to resembling or
were even remotely representative of a true violin.

As a professional violinist and teacher of violin and viola, Marilyn Worth
found this lack of authenticity to her favored instrument unendurable, so she
took herself to task and to the challenge of producing in miniature her beloved
violin.

The art of miniatures has been greatly enhanced by Worth's violins, which
are individually signed. The making of each instrument requires a minimum
of 40 hours of intensive dedication to detail, for the making of a scaled counterpart is an exacting craft. The photo on this page is enlarged to show detail.
For a more true size and appreciation of the subtle shadings of woods, see *Col-
or Plate 17.* (Refer to SOURCES for custom order information)
Photo: Dave Hammel; Author's collection

PLATE 9
These German hallmarked sterling silver pieces, (ca. 1880), originally belonged
in the personal collection of Mrs. James A. Bailey's miniatures. Mrs. Bailey
is related to Bailey of the world-famous Ringling Bros., Barnum and Bailey
Circus, (1810-1891).
Top Row: pair of arm chairs, measuring 1"x1". Highly engraved and meticulous
repousse work is evident in the 1"x2" *settee* or love seat.
Bottom Row: Dining table, 1¼"x2¾"x2", with four ¾"x¾" dining chairs. (See
SOURCES)
Photo: Dave Hammel; Jenny Biddle Collection

PLATE 10
"PETS IN MINIATURE" by Sue Dennis.
Sue's background in the field of animal husbandry and her subsequent training in arts and crafts, is highly apparent in her renditions of household pets. The "Three is Company", (Kittens in a Basket), is a limited edition of 3,000. The mantle piece, Santa, is a first in a forthcoming line of Christmas figures. Send a SASE for local shops selling Sue's work, or you can buy direct from the artist, retail or wholesale. (See SOURCES and TINY TALES sections) *Photo: Chanan Photography, Mira Loma, CA*

PLATE 11

PLATES 11, 12, 13,14

The photographs on _Plates 11 through 14_, depict the special talent of Cecil Boyd, creator and maker of _Masterpiece Museum Miniatures_. Each vignette tells its own story, and that story relies on the imagination of the reader which cannot help but be stirred by these masterful miniatures.

Cecil Boyd's first job following her education at the University of Texas, Austin, (where she earned her Bachelor of Arts degree), was as fashion illustrator. Her attention to minute details qualified her for the precision required in doing medical illustrations, which then led to the area of education. Her graphic designs were in demand for museums, displays, and exhibits including dioramas of historical events. The latter required miniature people of a distinct period, which led to her own inimitable designs for museum miniatures.

By 1977, Cecil had found a media to meet her talents but when she sought 1″ scale people for mass production, she discovered none were available. To produce one-of-a-kind figures was very expensive, and after weeks of trial and error, she accepted the challenge of making scaled figures available to museums and miniaturists. She had been disenchanted early in this pursuit by any figure clothed in fabric, because she believed in keeping the figures to scale, and it was almost impossible to translate both figures and fabrics into scaled work. Very beautiful Sculpy, porcelain, and other media dollhouse dolls, were being

PLATE 12

made by artists who excelled in their fields, but Cecil found that the addition of fabrics, hair, and accessories, unfortunately could not remain flawless to scale. Exploring the field further, she concluded that the makers of military figures cast in metal with uniforms and equipment made *part of the mold*, was the answer. However, this worked fine for tiny military soldiers, arms, and attire, but anything made of metal scaled 1″-1′, would be entirely too weighty.

Cecil finally settled on a material to fill the need, and decided to produce people who would complement the magnificent dollhouses being made. She wanted figures worthy of the work the miniaturists put into their houses, and that these human figures should enhance and bring alive specific scenes. Her aim has been to produce a human figure, completely sculptured, with no moving parts or fabric, accurate to scale and in anatomical proportions, and to show these figures in a particularly historically true time-frame of dress, rather than in "high style". Cecil's people, in "common dress", as opposed to "city folk" seems to relate more honestly to dollhouses being created today and those manufactured in yesteryear. Cecil modelled her figures in poses that were relaxed, easy to group, and appear startlingly real. Priority was given her latter aim, so that in addition to her pieces being realistic, their presence and personality would cause many a dramatic encounter with the settings into which they were placed. They were to be the ultimate accessory in any room, and make a static setting sizzle with more than a mere stirring of life.

PLATE 13

Thus far, Cecil Boyd's MUSEUM MASTERPIECE MINIATURES are divided into four categories, with many more planned for the future: 1) Victorian and Edwardian (a time-lapse of 10-20 years); 2) Twenties and Thirties Groups; 3) No time period (general); 4) Historical Group (representative for each quarter century from 1776 to the present). The exception to Cecil's 30-35 human figures, is "fantasy people" such as Mr. & Mrs. Santa Claus. This was pure fun for the artist who oftentimes considers herself a stodgy history buff. The Christmas figures were her one first "fling into fantasy", which she hopes will eventually lead to creating fairies and elves. Many of these are in the research stages of development.

The standard pieces shown within the pages of this book, can be customized, such as the "shopping lady" on _Color Plate 11_, which was made more elegant and gray-haired at the author's request. Cecil enjoys doing custom work, and new color schemes for it breaks the routine work. Since miniaturists who make dollhouses are usually talented artists, Cecil suggests that they paint their own MASTERPIECE MUSEUM MINIATURES by ordering them _unpainted_. These sculptured people can be evenly painted-over since they are of an epoxy material. A "How-To", easy to follow instruction sheet is enclosed with unpainted figures, and Cecil welcomes letters or telephone calls if more information is required. Hand-painting is time consuming, but very rewarding. Anyone

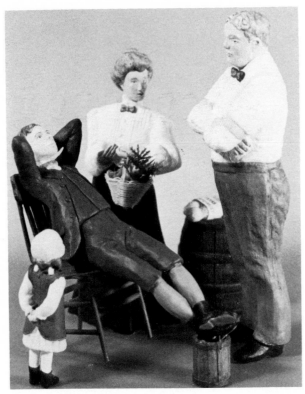

PLATE 14

who can do miniature work, wiring, construction, etc., can paint these figures
to his or her own liking. It's not a complicated process; it usually takes just
a bit of courage to get started, as with any other project. Men have been painting miniatures for years, such as soldiers and railroading memorabilia, and
many of those pieces are much smaller in scale than the human figures produced by Cecil Boyd.

The material used in the making of Cecil's figures, is an epoxy type of resin
which is very durable and workable for casting purposes. Using an X-Acto knife,
a file, or an emery board, one can make changes on the cast pieces. The molds
are cast from the artwork itself, and mold-making is both technical and ingenious, calling for a very special talent. Mold-making requires the perfection
usually assigned to jewelers.

Cecil researches clothing styles from a primary source, such as the yesteryear
Sears catalogues, as well as historical or period photographs that depict clothing
and accessories for a specific era. Devoted to precise 1″-1′ scale, Cecil Boyd's
MASTERPIECE MUSEUM MINIATURES are completely handcrafted in
America, of the highest quality workmanship, authentically costumed for the
miniature purist committed to period and scale accuracy. (See SOURCES &
VALUE GUIDE)

Photo credit: Plates 11 thru 14, courtesy Cecil Boyd

PLATE 15
Detailed section of "Keeping Room", with beamed ceiling. Walls are painted oyster-white. Rustic interior is achieved by use of random-width floor boards. This box-room, constructed by Roland Stieler, has custom furniture by Elwood Camp. Dode Trip's one-of-a-kind stoneware jugs, platter and copper mold, (hanging on wall), add to the mood of this quaint arrangement. Other brass pieces were purchased at various miniature shows.
Photo: KK Photos, Gig Harbor, WA; Stieler Collection

PLATE 16
This Victorian bedroom boasts a brass bed, appropriately dressed with quilted
spread and calico cloth pillows. Canopy & dust ruffle features eyelet fabric;
the curtains match the bedclothes. Miniaturist Dode Trip is credited with the
unique brass and marble plant stand. The fine rocking chair was purchased
in the 1930's. Bed frame available from Miniature House, Seattle, WA. Period
slippers by The Doll Cobbler.
Photo: KK Photos, Gig Harbor, WA; Stieler Collection

PLATE 17
Interior section of "Pioneer Cabin", showing the beamed ceiling, wide plank floors, and panelled wall. These are complemented by the excellent choice of authentic patterned wallpaper and the period fireplace. The mantle was purchased at the House of Miniatures, Seattle, WA; Elwood Camp made the Windsor chairs for a spartan table acquired in California in 1938.
Photo: KK Photos, Gig Harbor, WA; Stieler Collection

PLATE 18

Captured here is another view of the "Pioneer Cabin", highlighting the exposed beams, pair of Windsor chairs, and a primitive design Deacon 's Bench.
Elwood Camp made the set of Colonial clay pipes in a box which hangs near
the stone fireplace. These "Dutch" type smoking pipes are typical of those
available at Williamsburg Historic Monument, Virginia. A fine brass oil lamp
with glass hurricane dome was made by Dode Trip. Constance Stieler sewed
the braided rug and pillows from her own design. The Deacon's Bench is 1930's
manufacture.

Photo: KK Photos, Gig Harbor, WA; Stieler Collection

PLATE 19
A close-up picture of the "Pioneer Cabin", allows full appreciation of the
outstanding craftsmanship applied by Elwood Camp in the making of the pair
of Windsor chairs. For details of makers of braided rug, woodwork, and outstanding handmade clay pipes in storage box, see *Plates 17 and 18.*
Photo: KK Photos, Gig Harbor, WA; Stieler Collection

PLATE 20
"WILLIAMSBURG DRAWING ROOM"-Authenticity was gained by the use
of wide planks for flooring plus handmade paneling and molding. Mantlepiece
by Elwood Camp, was a gift made especially for this elegant setting. Walls
are painted Williamsburg blue; "Governor's Palace, Williamsburg" patterned
wallpaper is blue & white, available from the House of Miniatures, as are the
kits. (See SOURCES) Upholstery is cream-color silk; petitpoint rug is from
China. Elwood & Sally Camp made the petitpoint decorative firescreen. Bird-
cage tilt-top table: Lee Lener. Canton China "export" bowl: Chestnut Hill. Note
English handblown "cotton-twist" stem glass; Peking glass urn; antique sterling teapot, and "Ivory Jar" on center of mantle. The "jar" is an ivory bead
from India w/teakwood base & lid designed by Dode and Rudi Trip.
Photo: KK Photos, Gig Harbor, WA; Stieler Collection

PLATE 21

Recreating in miniature their California home, was the joint venture of Constance & Roland Stieler. Roland built the structure, cut the shingles and siding, made the workable windows, and formed the chimney of plywood. Constance then "built" the chimney of Sculpta Mold, scored the mold, and when perfectly dry she painted the "brick" with acrylic paints. Typical Williamsburg colors of deep beige, brown shutters and doors, add a Colonial charm to the miniature house. Although the windows and shutters were all handmade, the charming front door was purchased at Miniature House, Seattle, Washington. The "brick" foundation and steps are also hand done with Sculpta Mold.
Photo: KK Photos, Gig Harbor, WA; Stieler Collection

PLATE 22

Created by Roland Stieler, this "Log Cabin" was decorated and furnished by Constance Stieler. Pioneer motif necessitated unique pieces such as exterior "logs" made of wooden dowels, split in half. The shake-type roof exhibits individual pieces, hand cut, as were the floor planks and planked cabin door. Brown stain was used, "aged" by rubbing ashes on to the raised portions of the wood. The cowboy boots set on the outside porch are of genuine tooled leather, and are antique, as is the iron lantern in foreground. A pot-belly stove can be seen in a portion of the interior. For detailed photographs of this miniature dwelling, see *Plates 17, 18, and 19.*

Photo: KK Photos, Gig Harbor, WA; Stieler Collection

PLATE 23
The GAZEBO kit was made by Ted Miksovsky, available at "Jody's Shoppe",
6825 112th St., East, Puyallup, Washington 98373. Ted and his wife own the
shop and also build beautiful Victorian miniature houses. For information:
Phone 206-848-7996. Roland Stieler put together this kit which sets on a brick
base. It is furnished with white "wrought iron" glass-topped table and matching chairs. The pitcher and glasses are made by a local glassblower in Gig
Harbor, WA. The baskets of 1:12″ scale yellow roses, are from Denmark. The
outdoor furniture is from the Enchanted Dollhouse, P.O. Box 2047, 3259 SW
Highway 101, Lincoln City, OR 97367. Baskets of roses are available from Peter-
son's Chalet-in-the-Woods, 5231 Ray Nash Dr., NW, Gig Harbor, WA 98335.
Photo: KK Photos, Gig Harbor, WA; Stieler Collection

PLATE 24
VICTORIAN COTTAGE-all original wood shingles, siding, and window frames
by Roland Stieler, who also hand-turned the posts and spindles on his lathe.
The roof trim, "gingerbread" accents, plus central large porch-post were purchased at a mini "lumber yard". The elaborate front door: House of Miniatures,
Seattle, Washington. The woodwork on the exterior of the cottage was
deliberately "nicked" to give it an "aged" appearance. Painted in sunny yellow
with white trim, this mini-cottage has windows that can slide open for better
viewing of the interior which was designed, painted, and decorated by Constance
Stieler. Most of the Victorian furnishings were purchased at various miniature
shows.
Photo: KK Photos, Gig Harbor, WA; Stieler Collection

PLATE 25
Detailed corner of the "Keeping Room", a box-room created and constructed by Roland Stieler. Elwood Camp crafted the furniture, ably capturing the staid pioneer period pieces. Rug by Constance Stieler. See _Plate 15_ for another view of this droll setting.
Photo: KK Photos, Gig Harbor, WA; Stieler Collection

PLATE 26
The "Sun Room" in this dollhouse successfully accomplishes the indoor-outdoor look by exterior landscaping which is visible from within the room. The half-dollar coin shows 1:12″ scaled furniture. Compare the rattan furniture in this room with the pieces shown on *Plate 27*, (below), which are one-quarter inch to the foot scale.
Photo: Audrey Madans; Mr. & Mrs. Neil Heaslip Collection

PLATE 27
The ¼″ scale wicker furniture pieces were designed and made by Jinx Lee Theisen. The USA postage stamp allows the viewer to fully appreciate the teeny smallness of the couch, chair, plant stand, and round table--all easily accomodated in the palm of ones hand, and room to spare! Into this setting is placed an electrified ceramic Christmas Tree, designed by Joe Hermes and made by Mary Wary. (Tree not included in price of wicker.) The "fern" plant and table accessories were also made by Jinx, who is the designer and maker of the VIP's (*Very Important Pigs* dolls), such as "Little Red Riding Hog"; "Lady Ham-ilton"; "Lord Nel-swine", and many others in this popular series. (See SOURCES for address, or contact Jinx by phone: 213-539-8846.)
Photo: Dave Hammell; Jinx Lee Theisen Collection

PLATE 28
SAN FRANCISCO
ITALIANTE VICTORIAN.
Dollhouse shell was purchased
in December 1976, and Jim and
"Skip" Adair subsequently built
on a three-room addition. The
house is painted beige accented
in white, Colonial blue, and red
trimming.
Photo: KK Photos, Gig Harbor,
WA; Mrs. James "Skip" Adair
Collection

PLATE 29
Miniaturist "Skip" Adair, painted, wallpapered, electrically wired, laid hardwood floors, put in all the woodwork and trim, and also installed the door and windows in this dollhouse. Commercially made, are the master-bedroom suite, cradle, dining room table and chairs, china and silverware. Living room purchases include the fireplace, chandelier, spring-rocker, and violin. Accessories were handmade and created by Mrs. Adair, with additional purchases of dresser and brass bed, dog and Victrola for the boy's room; golden oak claw & ball table, pressed back chair, cradle, and ironing board for the kitchen. All the rooms have a "lived-in" look. For detailed pictures, see *Plates 30 thru 37.*
Photo: KK Photo, Gig Harbor, WA; Mrs James "Skip" Adair Collection

PLATE 30
A very special room for "Skip" Adair, it is filled with nostalgia and sentiment. Two "surprise" granddaughters were born in February and March 1979, and "Skip" sewed each a very ruffled dress, bonnet and panty. From the excess pink rosebud printed material and pink lace trimming, "Skip" made the canopy, bedspread and curtains for this charming room. Bedroom suite is commercial kit. Young girl figure, by Sylvia Lyons. Mary Haworth's crochet rug is in pinks and yellows. Cradle is a plastic shower "favor" given to "Skip" by her son, Jim Jo, who started "Skip" on her adventure into miniature-land. All other pieces were purchased at various hobby and miniature shops and shows.
Photos: KK Photos, Gig Harbor, WA; Mrs. James "Skip" Adair Collection

PLATE 31 (Page 40)
Interior scene of dollhouse shown on *Plate 29*. Chair, lamps, and drapes designed and made by "Skip" Adair; table, hallstand, and rug were made by "Skip" from commercial kits. Other purchases: chandelier, spring-rocker, and violin.
Photos: KK Photos, Gig Harbor, WA; Mrs. James "Skip" Adair Collection

PLATE 32 (Page 40)
Commercial kits provided the makings of a stove, sewing machine, chair and dress form. "Skip" Adair made the pots of red flowers, curtains, sewing basket and pincushion, as well as the crochet red, white and blue rug. Another of "Skip's" handiwork, the red gingham tablecloth, gives a homey touch to this busy scene. Her brother, Paul Haworth, made the "pie" cooling on the stove and the "bread" on the table.
Photos: KK Photos, Gig Harbor, WA; Mrs. James "Skip" Adair Collection

PLATE 31

PLATE 32

PLATE 33 (see page 42)

PLATE 34 (see page 42)

PLATE 35

PLATE 33
Human figures bring a room alive, and those shown in these pictures were made by Sylvia Lyons. Handmade items include lamps and framed shell collection, as well as the "Bear" rug made from rabbit skin. Commercially purchased: dresser, brass bed, books, train set, dog and Victrola. Night stands were made from kit. Bed-clothes were painstakingly quilted by "Skip" Adiar, who also made the matching curtains.
Photos: KK Photos, Gig Harbor, WA; Mrs. James "Skip" Adair Collection

PLATE 34
"Skip" wallpapered the rooms, and laid the commercially bought woodwork. The brass vase is filled with flowers picked from a local tree, then dried. Commercial kits include: Oriental rug, wallshelf, tea cart, and hanging light fixtures. "Turkey" on the table, by Paul Haworth. The china cabinet, (kit), displays many souvenirs, and the table is set with Imari-design dishes. The dining room chairs were purchased already assembled by an unknown maker.
Photos: KK Photos, Gig Harbor, WA; Mrs. James "Skip" Adair Collection

PLATE 35
Mother and infant by Sylvia Lyons look very much in place in this Victorian bedroom suite with cradle. These were commercially purchased by "Skip" Adair, who then completed the lamps, table, and two matching chairs from "scratch", using a jig-saw and X-Acto knives. Tablecloth and chair covers are covered in raw silk, as are the quilt and pillows. Handmade curtains are of lovely antique lace. Rug is painted with pencils on cream-colored velvet to blend with the wallpaper. The pictures on the walls are period photographs (miniaturized) of "Skip's" mother and an aunt.
Photos: KK Photos, Gig Harbor, WA; Mrs. James "Skip" Adair Collection

PLATE 36
The Victorian Parlor is captured in all its elegance and period styling. Figure by Sylvia Lyons. The _cloisonne_ vase was purchased in San Francisco's Chinatown. Made from commercial kits: organ, table, and Oriental carpet. "Skip" Adair handmade from "scratch" the living room suite, lamp, and Valentine heart-shaped box of candy on the table and the look-alive "Spider" plant. She made the table lamp from jewelry findings, and made the furniture with a jig-saw and X-Acto knife. The lovely chandelier was purchased along with the ornate mirror frame which was gilded, and a bevelled custom-cut piece of mirror was set into the frame. It was tastefully hung to reflect the beautiful portrait on the opposite wall.
Photo: KK Photos, Gig Harbor, WA; Mrs. James "Skip" Adair Collection

PLATE 37
When "Skip" Adair's husband, Jim, bought her the various Sylvia Lyons' dolls for her dollhouse, they were all dressed except the grandfather figure, so "Skip" decided to try her hand at costume, with excellent results. This view of the Victorian parlor shows the chairs and drapes of soft blue velvet, handmade by "Skip". The walls are covered in raw silk purchased in the Orient by a friend who gave it as a gift for "Skip's" project. Note how very effectively the house-number "1976" shows through the lighting from the outside. Also note the details of the classic and popular spring-rocker chair with its scaled doilies. The exterior of this room can be seen in *Plate 28.*
Photo: KK Photos, Gig Harbor, WA; Mrs James "Skip" Adair Collection

PLATE 38

"PATTI'S HAT SHOP". Patti Highfill made the stylish chapeau displayed in her adorable little shop. Inside the counter case are crochet purses, and a 1″ square handkerchief with crochet edging made of 140 weight thread. On display is a pair of French kidskin gloves, with each finger of the glove hand-sewn to perfection. All of the shop accessories, including the clock, hat boxes, perfume bottles, lamp, etc., were made by talented Patti Highfill, who is a charter member of N.A.M.E. (National Association of Miniature Enthusiasts, founded in 1972). Her background as artist and craftswoman comes in good stead as she employs her skills to the mastery of porcelain techniques, petit-point, crochet, and painting everything from dolls' faces to tole patterns on tiny wooden chairs. More of Patti's work can be seen on *Plates 62 thru 68.*
Photo: Detailed enlargement by Dave Hammell from a photo by Dale Fink; Patti and Paul Highfill Collection

PLATE 39
Porcelain jointed miniature dolls by Stephanie Blythe, dressed in silk flowers
by Stephanie and Susan Snodgrass. The two talented mini-makers have col-
laborated in making wee fairies and dolls for almost three years. From their
realm of fantasy come these enchanting "Flower Children". These imaginative
figures represent the talents of two academically trained and experienced artists.

Stephanie Blythe's professional designer techniques are utilized in dressing
the dolls in silk flower petals. The actual doll is created by Susan Snodgrass,
whose early artistic ability rooted itself in the Chicago Art Institute, home of
the famous and fabulous Thorne Rooms.

Both Stephanie and Susan work to create and capture something tangible
in the intangible substance found in the aura of reverie and fantasy. Their forte
is in scaled vignettes rather than in definitive rooms. Fairy tales and storybook
characters spring magically to life from their seemingly overflowing fountains
of fantasy and frolic; their figures *live* in enchanted settings. (See SOURCES
and TINY TALES sections)

Photo: Todd Black; Stephanie Blythe & Susan Snodgrass Collections

PLATE 40
A DOLLHOUSE FOR CHRISTMAS. Christmas morning, 1979, was a very
special event in the author's life. A miniature dollhouse kit purchased "on sale"
from _Lynne's Miniature Treasures_ catalogue, had arrived mid-summer, and the
garage became Santa's workshop. The dollhouse shell was completed, minus
doors and "gingerbread", but it was the beginning of a longtime dream come
true. The structure held great promise although much remodeling had to be
done. The "nine room house" originally had the staircase imposing itself in
the parlor then landing in the upstairs bedroom. This would never do! Not in
the period Victorian-Edwardian mansion planned by the author. The laborious
task of reassembling each step and reversing the entire staircase, took a great
deal of industry and ingenuity, for the stair wells that formerly intruded into
the aforementioned rooms had to be closed off and a new opening made in the
entry hall. This one important change began the transformation from a commercially prepared dollhouse kit into an Edwardian mansion. _(See Color Plate 1)_
_Photo: Black & White print by Dave Hammell, from a color shot by Lillian
Baker; Mr. & Mrs. R.A. Baker Collection_

PLATE 41
Closeup shot of chimney for THE VANE EAGLE mansion. Inverted wall plugs
with the screwhole covered with a jewelry finding, give the impression of "clay"
dual chimmey pipes. A metallic French button serves as a central accent; pointed
end of antique clock hand sets atop a "Golden Arches" insigna which originally served as a stir-stick. Foreground shows black plastic "wrought iron" unpainted; in rear is a painted Widow's Walk. Chimney is original design and constructed by the author. Seagulls are souvenir of trip along Oregon Coast.
Photo: Dave Hammell

PLATE 42
The beginnings of a staircase in construction stage. For completed project, see _Color Plate 2._
Photo: Dave Hammell, from color shots by Lillian Baker.

PLATE 43
Remodeling continued in THE VANE EAGLE, with the installation of a high window in the dining room. The original kit contained design for front window only. Cutting into the side wall, and using a narrow horizontal rather than a vertical opening, provided interior and exterior with a more interesting architectural feature. _(See Plate 45)_
Photo: Dave Hammell, from color shots by Lillian Baker

PLATE 44
Closeup of individual shingling and contrived weather-vane which gives the Baker mini-mansion its name: THE VANE EAGLE. The coin-shaped center piece on the weathervane's tiny billet, caps off the opening of a pencil sharpener which originally came in a coppertone pot metal. The directional letters, Eagle, and arrow (made from two different style antique clock hands), have been gilded. The Widow's Walk in this photo has been painted Victorian Grey (or Llama Grey). The larger foreground "wrought iron" is plastic; the smaller scale is metal. The slant, shingled roof seen on the right side of the photo, is the attic with an unshaded light bulb (electrified) shining on a myriad of objects, including a ca. 1876 Centennial American Flag 1:12″ scale. A trunk, lampshades, "sad" irons, and other paraphernalia crowd the attic, suggesting that this loft is for storing both materials and memories.
Photo: Dave Hammell

PLATE 45

Author's hand gives contrast to the actual size of the wood lathe siding, high dining room window, and additional "gingerbread" of a detailed portion of THE VANE EAGLE miniature mansion. (See _Color Plate 1_, for exterior view, and _Color Plate 13_ for interior view of section of dining room.) A collection of fine handblown colored glass, including a cobalt bell, are displayed on inside sill. Outside sill is used for blooming "Christmas Cactus", handmade from bits of green plastic, with blooms painted white. On the trio of plant-rests, are three handmade, painted, geraniums. The plastic gingerbread comes from market baskets originally packed with strawberries and tomatoes. Many of these plastic "crates" are most decorative and can be easily cut apart, applied to the dollhouse with white glue, and then painted along with the wood decorative pieces. The wonderful thing about a miniature mansion is that there's no "right" or "wrong" way. Surely there's satisfaction in doing it "your way".

Photo: Dave Hammell

PLATE 46

Barbara Kalty's expertise was gained through her formal training and background in jewelry making. The brass tricycle wheels spin and turn in all directions, and the handle grips actually come off. The fireplace tools, all hand wrought by Barbara, show the same precision used in watch-making. As with the fireplace implements, the baby-buggy or doll carriage is made of brass, and is functional. The adorable baby-doll, dressed in crochet habit, is by Patti Highfill. (See SOURCES)

Photo: Dave Hammell; Barbara Kalty Collection

PLATE 47

A Kennedy commemorative half-dollar dwarfs wee engine coal-car of the toy locomotive that turns round its track. The larger brass train is 1"-1' scale; center toy is ¼" scale. The Christmas Tree turns on its axis when the "paddles" above are blown upon. When it spins, the angel touches the brass ornaments and makes a delightful "ting". Candles are wax. This mini-masterpiece is all brass.

Photo: Dave Hammell; Barbara Kalty Collection

PLATE 48

Barbara Kalty works in wood as well as brass, and achieves perfection in both media. (*See Plates 46-47*) The walnut dining room table and six chairs, have a matching hutch (not shown), and are replicas of the full-sized dining suite in Barbara's home. The dining table's leaf can be removed and the table made smaller. Dried floral centerpiece, also handmade by Barbara, is a copy of larger decoration. Silver punchbowl, ladel, tray and punchcups, from the author's collection, ordered from Willoughby Taylor, Ltd., (see CATALOGUES).
Photo: Dave Hammell; Barbara Kalty Collection

PLATE 49

The children's bedroom, living room, and dining room furniture in the Kalty household, have been miniaturized to 1/12" scale by the talented housewife, mother, and mini-master, Barbara Kalty. Among the replicas is the perfectly scaled convertible backgammon table, with an inlaid wood playing board, (reverse side is for chess and is patterned like the folding chairs). In foreground, next to Kennedy half-dollar coin, is ½" scaled checkerboard with boxful of checkers. Woods used are walnut, pine, and mahogany. Chairs actually fold.
Photo: Dave Hammell; Barbara Kalty Collection

PLATE 50

Miriam Irwin's MOSAIC PRESS, has been publishing miniature books for more than five years. Readable type on acid-free paper, the books are hand-sewn with linen thread and bound with the same exquisite care given to works of the masters in the finest hand-bound full size editions. Pictured in the palm of the photographer, (who held camera in her other hand), is "THE CROWN JEWELS", written by Karen Feinberg in honor of the Cincinnati Art Museum's *Tower of London* exhibit. The text is enriched with pen-and-ink drawings by Romilda Dilley. Shown on open page is the crown originally made for Queen Victoria in 1837. (Compare this crown with Barbara Bunce's creations, *Plate 81*.) This grand miniature edition has gold stamping on its navy cloth binding, with top gilding and blue and white marbled end sheets. The book measures 15/16" high, 64 pages.

Photo: Courtesy, Susan R. Seigneuret, Associate Editor, "Millcreek Valley News", Cincinnati, Ohio 45212

PLATE 51

Three 15/16" high books providing versatility of subject matter: *OSHA SPECS: re the Fetus; The Grandparent Book;* and *Corals of Pennekamp.*

Photo: Joel Fingerman

PLATE 52
KEEPSAKE BOOK BOX created by champion bookbinder, Hugo Grummich, was made to hold a collection of *Mosaic Press* books. The leather book-box has the words *Miniature Books* stamped in gold on the ornate spine and cover. It includes a plexiglas insert to safely guard and display the precious handmade miniature books. Because it measures 6¼″ wide, 7½″ tall, and 1½″ deep, it can readily be hidden among other books on a standard bookshelf, when it is not on display.
Photo: Joel Fingerman

PLATE 53
The lore and history of 24 breeds of dogs, arranged in alphabetical order, appears in the 3/volume set of *DOGS*, written by Jeanne Eichling, with each dog illustrated by Roy Moore. Tan cloth w/marbled end papers, 15/16″ tall.
Photo: Dave Michaelis

PLATE 54
The turn-of-the-century Bride & Groom sepia studio portrait, has been reduced to 1″-1′ scale by a special miniaturization process. The ornate rococo frame, was much favored for wedding pictures of yesteryear. It is shown being gilded in antique gold finish.
Photo: Leonard Nadel; Evelyn DeWolf Nadel Collection

PLATE 55
Enlarged to show detail, this three-dimensional _collage_ brings together several patriotic symbols of the American Revolution. So perfectly done, it appears to be a painting rather than a 3-D picture. Note contrast in size of regular wire hanging picture screw and wee hanging loop attached to this wooden frame. (Maker unknown)
Photo: Leonard Nadel; Evelyn DeWolf Nadel Collection

PLATE 56
Stephen Goode designed and constructed the walnut cradle 1:12″ scale, exactly as he had crafted full-size cradles for the children in his family and to sell at "swap meets" at Christmastime to earn "stocking stuffin'money". When Steve delved into mini-making, it seemed only natural that he try to capture his original design in miniature. The crochet bedclothes and blankets in the walnut chest, were made by Bonnie Goode. (See SOURCES & CATALOGUES section) The walnut blanket chest with burl walnut hinged cover, is a 1:12″ scaled copy of Bonnie's cedar chest. Steve fashioned the working metal hardware so that the bent-wood shelf opens with the lid. The beautiful chest has .020″ joints, precision crafted. The oak side chair, by master woodcraftsman, Verl Kraeger, is one of three added each Christmas to the Goode's miniature collection. Kraeger's chairs are Steve's Christmas gift to Bonnie, purchased at Alice's Imagination Shop. (See SOURCES)

The piecrust tilt-top walnut table, has Macassar ebony legs whose dense black color is broken by its dark brown streaks which lends a pleasing pattern differing from a true ebony which is coal black to brown black with almost no pattern but is rather hard and very dense. Stephen Goode has used professional tongue and groove construction in the making of this fine miniature table.

In the foreground is a Victorian sewing basket, with all its "necessaries" such as scissors, buttons, needles, pins, and familiar "tomato" pincushion. Note the satin ribbon woven through the crochet loops. (*Color Plate 12* shows this 1″ classic period piece with closed lid.) The exquisite work was done by Vivian Litsch and is available by special order through the "Many Goode's" mail-order catalog. (See CATALOGUES)

(Baby in cradle is by Cecil Boyd, from the author's collection. See *Color Plates 8 and 9*.)

Photo: Dave Hammell; Stephen and Bonnie Goode Collection

PLATE 57
Bookcase-desk combination in golden oak by "Reminiscence", makers of fine miniature furniture for mini-shop distribution.
Porcelain "Bride & Groom" traditional figurine under glass dome, is signed "B.N., 1980".
Photo in wood frame is author's mother, reprinted from an old sepia picture, ca. 1915. Reduced to scale by Dave Hammell.
Photo: Dave Hammell; Author's Collection

PLATE 58
This unique walnut hardwood chair is an original design by LaNeva Peacock, who tutored Clare Albert enabling her to cut, shape, and glaze-coat-finish this project.

The curved hood, made of needlepoint canvas, is shaped to custom fit, then stained with walnut color to simulate woven cane work.

Needlepoint flame-stitch design is on olive green canvas and is upholstered over a foam rubber cushion.
Photo: Dave Hammell; Clare Albert Collection

PLATE 59

Side chair, carved wood, lacquered and handpainted in the Republic of China. (Rear view shown on _Color Plate 12_). Purchased at Gim Fong's shop, Los Angeles.

Desk chair, golden oak, by "Fantastic Merchandise", maker of fine miniatures. Side chair or boudoir chair, covered in slipper satin. Hand-carved rosewood. Marked: "Made Exclusively for Handicraft Designs, Taiwan, R.D.C." (1½" across by 3" high)

Desk chair, approximately 2½" tall, _chinoiserie_ design, ca. 1800's. Hardwood and handpainted. Made in Republic of China and sold through Willoughby Taylor Ltd., International Merchants (catalogue).

Photo: Dave Hammell; Author's Collection

PLATE 60 (Page 62)

Handsome buffet or side board from Clare Albert's box-showcase "DINING ROOM". All original, including shaping, carving, and staining by Clare who chose basswood for this project. She slimmed down and _cabriole_-shaped the legs with a Dremel Moto-tool, which was also used for woodcarving.

Rug is a commercial kit on 18 gauge canvas. 5"x7" with ½" fringe. Rug is backed with iron-on fabric interfacing. Made by Clare Albert.

Blown glass punchbowl with cups and ladel are by "Glass Concepts", an Illinois based maker who distributes to mini-shops. Exquisite and rare blown glass candle holders with glass candlesticks are by an anonymous artist, and was purchased from Alice's Imagination Shop.

Photo: Dave Hammell; Accessories from Author's Collection. Side Board and rug from Clare Albert Collection

PLATE 61 (Page 62)

"DINING ROOM" box-showcase boasts this basswood desk, hand-painted with black enamel. Gold leaf was applied to commercially produced stencils; the gold stripes around the edges and the accenting of leg turnings, were applied freehand by maker, Clare Albert, who handmade the counted cross-stitch chair cover using #22 Hardanger. Pattern from "Charted Designs for Miniatures", by June Grigg.

Statue of Liberty clock, author's collection, by Patti Highfill. Williamsburg reproduction pewter inkwell w/feather, millefiori paperweight, and teeny Ben Franklin wire-frame type spectacles, are all from author's collection.

Photo: Dave Hammell; Desk and Chair, Clare Albert Collection

PLATE 60 (see page 61)

PLATE 61 (see page 61)

Color Photographs

Color Plates 1-24

COLOR PLATE 1
THE VANE EAGLE, Edwardian Mansion, (ca. 1918)
Unlike snow-laden lands depicted on traditional holiday cards, Southern California Christmas scenes show unique areas where flowers abound and orange trees yield abundant sun-ripened fruit. Warm valleys, protected by distant snow-capped mountains, create visual contrasts of awe-inspiring intensity.

Into this setting, the author has framed her miniature mansion which received its name from the one-of-a-kind weathervane, (shown in detail on *Plate 44*).

The mansion is custodian for tiny treasures or cherished gifts which were either store-bought or handmade. The attic is a depository for "duplicates" and authentic type memorabilia found in attics after the turn-of-the century when the "machine age" invaded private residences making "things" obsolete. Gaslight gave way to electricity; at long last there was indoor plumbing.

The permanent decor of the THE VANE EAGLE, is "getting ready for Santa" and "Christmas in California". Each of the color plates in this book relates to this theme. The author prepared each vignette aiming at achieving the human warmth, affection, and nostalgia which usually radiates from Victorian-Edwardian scenes of childhood. A *dollhouse* at Christmastime is doubly blessed because it keeps the Holiday Season yearlong; it need not be dismantled as does its full-size counterpart.

Dimensions; BASE, (disguised as a retaining wall), 36" x 24" x 6" high. MANSION, 29" across the front; 15" back to front; and 38" high, excluding the attic, which is 5" x 5" x 5" high. A FOUNDATION was added to the dollhouse, measuring 2½" all sides. STEPS: 2" high x 6½" wide. (Details of chimney, weathervane, and gingerbread, are shown on *Plates 41 thru 45*) Construction, including individual shingles, papering and wiring, were accomplished by author's husband, "Al" Baker. Additional designs for interior and exterior work, including landscaping, were done by the author.

Mansion has 24 working lights; hinged and workable front doors and upstairs "French Doors" leading to the balcony. Front doors have hand-etched and beveled glass. Much of the gingerbread was achieved by masquerading plastic shower curtain hooks, buttons, shells, beads, clock hands, and a myriad of metallic findings cleverly camouflaged as highly decorative accents.

The Edwardian lady, carrying a potted plant made entirely of wood (German), is a custom piece by Cecil Boyd, the extraordinary artist of Masterpiece Museum Miniatures. (*See Plates 11 thru 14*) This figure has been named, "Grandmother Anne Katherine". (Names for dollhouse figures are author's choice). Outdoor scenic *collage*, (used as backdrop), by the author.
Photo: Dave Hammell

COLOR PLATE 2

Entryhall to THE VANE EAGLE miniature mansion. The little daughter, Missy, holding her favorite ragdoll behind her back, knows Christmas and Santa are coming because of the holiday garland decorating the staircase. (Little figure w/doll by Cecil Boyd). Christmas garland w/ribbons by the author.

Steps leading up to the porch, were first constructed of wood by Al Baker; they were then covered with several layers of "roughed up" *paper mache'*, to give them the appearance of heavy, worn, stone.

California at Christmastime, and one can pick several of the ripe oranges for breakfast just by reaching out the front door and over the porch of THE VANE EAGLE.

The "hinge" on an improvised front gate, was an unidentifiable "find" on the street; it appeared as if it could serve as a one-piece latch. When it was gilded, it converted imagination into reality.

The brass knobs and added decorative wood pieces to the doors, have introduced the new transition from Art Nouveau of Edwardian era, to Art Deco, plus achieving a "heavy look" to the front doorway.

Because the stairway was relocated and reversed, thus leaving an open-end to each stair, improvisation required special decorative objects, handmade posts, knobs, and rails, all custom designed and worked by hand by the author and her husband. This was one of the more challenging parts of the project, which was a joint venture.

Note the "Tiffany" lighted chandelier, purchased from Alice's Imagination Shop, as was the potted poinsettia on brass stand. Flowers in clay pot, (foreground), are completely wooden, made in Germany. Green-leafed plant in old miniature Japanese vase, was made by the author. Outside porch lamp, from Lynne's Miniature Treasures (catalog). A "welcome mat" rests on outside porch doorway; the fringed rug in entryway, is an original design, handpainted and fringed by the author. (Detail on *Cover* and *Color Plate 10)* Stairway is carpeted in self-adhesive gold velour Contact paper. Halltree/chair combination by *Reminiscene in Miniature*, available thru most miniature shops. This piece was purchased at Alice's Imagination Shop. (See SOURCES).

Photo: Dave Hammell; Author's Collection

COLOR PLATE 3

Missy, and her favorite doll Mattie, explore the bustling kitchen which is an extension of THE VANE EAGLE mansion. The Stuart Library Showcase provides a temporary setting until the permanent box-room is completed, a room which will carry the theme of THE VANE EAGLE throughout its creation. The icebox, stove, cupboard, and drysink (not shown), were mastered by Al Baker from commercial kits.

A pierced brass French button makes an ideal vent covering for the wooden "stovepipe" which has been lengthened from the original kit specifications.

Corner open cupboard is a handcut piece, custom-made many years ago by an old gentleman for his little granddaughter. The kitchen worktable, with its old-fashioned tin flour bins, (see under open drawer), is from Lynne's Miniature Treasures catalog.

Many memories are revived and senses stirred, as we see Missy studying the Gingerbread House and other goodies in this homey kitchen. Floor is "Delft tile" patterned wallpaper. Pots and pans on the stove were originally silvercolor pot metal. They were painted by the author to suggest the old fashioned enamel "spatterware" cooking utensils. In one larger pan, the author has contrived "cranberries" at a slow sugary boil. This was achieved by the use of red beads dropped into rubber cement (used for paste-ups). The rubber cement is of such consistency it prevents the beads from sinking to the bottom; rather it gives a sugary, clouded appearance of a "slow boil".

Black "iron" wall match holder, three copper molds, and copper-colored tea kettle, all from Alice's Imagination Shop. Large single mold, antique brass pitcher, canned goods, etc., were gifts. The "Gold Medal" 25 pound sack of flour, was a gift from Shirlee Pierce, herself a talented and avid miniaturist.

Apples and peaches in baskets, by Gail Wise, available from *Many Goode's* catalogue, which also supplied the maple rolling pin, wood crates and baskets with other foodstuffs. The soda "on ice" in a bucket, the covered handblown glass cannisters, and the Christmas peppermint canes in one of the jars, are from Alice's Imagination Shop. Loaf of baked bread in a pan "cooling off" atop the stove, and the small round box of "Morton's Salt", are from Lynne's Miniature Treasures.

The "glazed ham" and other foodstuffs on the platter are from Mostly Miniatures, (See SOURCES); the tall "iced" layer cake with cherry topping, a gift from The Gypsy Merchant. The tall covered jar of peppermint sticks, and clay mini-pitchers on the corner cupboard, were acquired during the author's travels.

To avoid attracting ants or other types of crawlies, the author uses talcum powder to simulate "spilled" flour.

Photo: Dave Hammell; Author's Collection

COLOR PLATE 4
Throughout her stroll in this busy dollhouse mansion, little Missy has remembered to "look with your eyes, not with your hands". The adorable little girl figure by Cecil Boyd, is shown in another vignette created within the confines of the opposite end of The Stuart Library Showcase. (See *Color Plate 3)* "Tile" floor accentuates the authenticity of these bathroom fixtures which were put together from commercial kits by Al Baker, purchased from Alice's Imagination Shop.

The wood screen and black "heater" w/wire handle, plus the painted metal "waterbag" on edge of tub, were from Lynne's Miniature Treasures catalog.

The housepets are being given a tin-tub bath by Mrs. Primrose who serves the household as a live-in cook, household helper, and seamstress, and surely Missy's "confidante".

The mama dog in the tub, and her wee Chihuahua pup being dried with a towel, are bone china; the dog (foreground), scratching and awaiting its turn in the tub, is an old miniature "Made in Japan".

Note the toothbrush in a blown glass tumbler, the toothpaste, towels, towel bar, and lamp (not wired), and the "Ivory" soap wrapper. The roll of toilet paper w/dispenser and aforementioned accessories are 1":1' scale, and commercially purchased from Alice's Imagination Shop.

The "newspapers" on the floor under the tub, are miniature scaled reprints of *The New York Times*, 1918, available through many mini-catalogues and shops.

The water-closet above the toilet has a pullchain, all giving an "old fashioned" look to this setting. This bathroom will eventually be located off Mrs. Primrose's bedroom/sewing room. Other pieces in readiness, are shown on *Color Plate 12.*

Photo: Dave Hammell; Author's Collection

COLOR PLATE 5

Missy's bedroom/playroom is located on third floor directly above the master bedroom in THE VANE EAGLE Edwardian mansion. Look closely, and the reader will spot the pink-ribboned Missy studying her pet goldfish in the glass bowl atop her desk.

On this desk is a lighted brass Student Lamp, and bookends fashioned from dolls resembling "Raggedy Ann" and "Raggedy Andy". In the foreground, seated on a child's playchair, are dolls more in keeping with the recognized image of the characters created by Johnny Gruelle. Some authorities on dolls have stated that the stories and pictures of the familiar pair of character dolls, were inspired by a rag doll that belonged to Gruelle's mother. In fact, the author of those delightful "Raggedy Ann Stories", tells in the Preface and Dedication of the 1918 edition, that his mother's rag doll had provided "lessons of kindness and fortitude" and "wisdom of fifty nine years". It seems then, that the *model* for Raggedy Ann dolls which were first commercially manufactured in 1918, was ca. 1859! Interestingly enough, James Whitcomb Riley wrote a poem, "The Raggedy Man", which tells of a little boy's admiration of the "hired hand" who is also the beau of Lizabuth Ann in Riley's "Our Hired Girl". The aforementioned poem was written in 1890, and poses the question: did Lizabuth Ann evolve into "Raggedy Ann"; and did "The Raggedy Man" become "Raggedy Andy"? Several mini-makers have stated that a Raggedy Ann & Andy could not or should not be included in any dollhouse until post-1918. The above historical research should assist mini-makers in resolving that issue.

The ¼″ scaled dollhouse was purchased at Wind Bells Cottage, (unknown maker); the author handmade the bedclothes for a commercially made bedstead, as well as the Teddy w/paper hat seated on chair in foreground. Rug was designed, made, and handpainted in original pattern by the author, who also constructed and custom-made the furniture w/bookshelves against the back wall. The Teddy was a N.A.M.E. workshop project during the 1980 California Houseparty.

Note authentic scaled brass wall lamp w/glass globe, lighting the charming old-fashioned print of the perfectly scaled wallpaper. Wooden doll in cradle, is German. Other adorable dolls, Pug in Wagon, and jointed doll on bed are gifts of great sentiment to the author. The lace-covered, hooded buggy and "Tiffany" lamp with shade are available from Lynne's Miniature Treasures. For addresses of additional suppliers, see SOURCES.

Photo: Dave Hammell; Author's Collection

COLOR PLATE 6

Decorating the Christmas Tree. The shell for this display is an original by Stephen Goode. He structured the walls of this room box with his own flooring and baseboard molding. The richness he achieved is by his use of pink *peroba* * and magnolia border inlay, plus gum flooring, all available from S.H. Goode & Sons Workshop. (See SOURCES). The hearth's simulated brick is holly (wood) stained with floquil rosewood stain, then grooved in a brick pattern.

On the mantle: (Left to Right) ½"H Victorian frame w/portrait; hand-blown ruby glass w/applied handle; Christmas arrangement, (painted toothpicks represent candles); scaled 1/12" daguerreotype by Joan Helton, (see SOURCES); and blown glass decorator piece.

The crochet garland was a gift to author; crochet stockings available from Bonnie Goode and Alice's Imagination Shop. Framed needlepoint, dated and initialed by maker, Clare Albert, reads: "When this you see, remember me", especially made for the author as a birthday gift. Fireplace screen, gilded wood and metal, by the author. Bevelled mirror, decorated with ¼" wreath, purchased at N.A.M.E. Convention.

Christmas tree, decoration, and crochet tree skirt, all by Bonnie Goode. Skirt made w/tatting thread; design from old photo. Hand-painted lead dog w/metal shoe, from Alice's Imagination Shop. Candle table made by George Baker; centerpiece by Vivian Litsch, (available thru *Many Goode's* catalogue).

Mini crochet doilies by Bonnie Goode. Figure w/basket of Christmas ornaments, by Cecil Boyd (Masterpiece Museum Miniatures). Swan Chair, (foreground), by well-known mini-master, Susanne Russo. This work of art is handcarved from Alder wood, richly stained with a high gloss that accentuates details. Susanne Russo is reached at: Memory Maker Shop, 305 N. Fifth St., Clarksburg, West Virginia 26301. Side Chair, (back wall), was carved by Stephen Goode, from Boxwood; 14 separate pieces of wood were pinned with lathe-turned *Lignum Vitae* .020" pins. Carolee Rowley did the needlepoint work on 52 mesh canvas, requiring 2,704 stitches to the inch! (Chair and needlepoint original Goode designs. Swan and Side chairs from Goode collection).

Christmas wrapped packages under the tree, by Cynthia Herrmann. (See SOURCES) What appears to be another wrapped package, (under side chair, rear), is actually a souvenir lapel pin given as a gift to the author by mini-maker Jo-An of Jo-Ann Imports, one of the many exhibitors at N.A.M.E. Houseparty, 1982. N.A.M.E. is an excellent source for contacting artisans who specialize in specific miniatures. (See THUMBNAIL SKETCH)

The low dessert table made of ironwood, was designed and crafted by Stephen Goode for Bonnie Goode collection.

*Pink *peroba* is a very rare Brazilian wood. It's also known as red *peroba* and *peroba rosa*. It is seldom listed, but can be found and identified in *Timbers of the World*, published by TRADA, The Construction Press Ltd., Lancaster, England, (1980).
Photo: Dave Hammell; Author's Collection unless otherwise noted

COLOR PLATE 7

From the kitchen of THE VANE EAGLE, comes the baked goodies seen on this "wrought iron" Baker's Rack, all made by the author either from a hobby type "bread dough", or by using a commercial mold that has been filled with plaster-of-Paris. Once the latter hardened, it was removed and painted according to whim or fancy.

TOP SHELF: typical powdered anise cookies made by using the end of a straw as a "cookie-cutter". To remove, the author blew on the other end of the straw, then layered each round on a handpainted plastic disc. The final "powdered" look was achieved with white gesso paint, *unglazed*. The centerpiece shows a recognizable copy of a blue and white Danish Christmas Plate, but this mini-plate is plastic. The paper doily is the center of a dessert-sized doily available at most Hallmark card shops. We see an open "cherry pie", handpainted plaster-of-Paris, then glazed with an acrylic clear spray.

MIDDLE SHELF; baked French bread and twisted bread made of "play" dough; plaster-of-Paris mold, scored and painted. The loaves of bread are on small linen nappies which are linen *applique* pieces.

BOTTOM SHELF: A Christmas *stollen*, iced and decorated by the author, and an upside-down cake, both of play bread-dough. Many miniature books give recipes for making this inexpensive bread dough which can be stored in plastic bags until ready to work with as schedule permits.

A household wooden match, (foreground) provides the reader with a clue to scale-size of items in this picture. It is on the parlor rug which was handmade and painted by the author from an original design. It can be seen in its proper place on *Color Plate 14*.

The Christmas wrappings, tablecloth, and workable Nutcracker, have come out of attic storage, as has the 1":1' Santa Claus suit, made by the author from a workshop pattern suppled at an early N.A.M.E. Houseparty. However the belt buckle is one saved from a wardrobe that belonged to "Barbie", a doll w/accessories that once was a favorite plaything of the author's daughter, Wanda.

The Christmas wrapped package was done by Cynthia Herrmann, purchased at Mostly Miniatures, as was the box of Christmas ornaments. (See SOURCES)

Baker's Rack (approx. 5½"H) w/goodies, Jenny Biddle Collection
Photo: Dave Hammell; Author's Collection, unless otherwise noted

COLOR PLATE 8
Several of the items shown on this Plate have been described in the text accompanying *Color Plate 5*. This picture provides an opportuity to admire the fine detail of the many artisans' work.
TOP ROW: Patti Highfill's baby in hand-crochet dress, bonnet, and booties. (See *Plate 67*, and refer to SOURCES) Seated on rustic children's chairs, are two dolls by a doll-artist whose one-of-a-kind children's play-dolls scaled to dollhouse-size, are held in great esteem by everyone who has had an opportunity to purchase them at N.A.M.E. Houseparties. Unfortunately, the author cannot identify the maker by name, but her sales-agent is kept extremely busy at the booth in which the artist's work is sold. Standing in front of the ¼ " scale dollhouse, (see *Color Plate 5*), is another rendition of those popular rag dolls, "Raggedy Ann" and "Raggedy Andy", 3/8" tall. The chairs are companion pieces to a child's table, and are Mexican imports.
BOTTOM ROW: 3" handpainted china, incised mark: "Made in Japan", of a little girl holding a doll. A smaller version of this "penny doll", (actually standing on a U.S. copper 1-cent piece), is a 1½" version reproduced for miniaturists by unknown maker. The assortment of adorable handmade "bread dough" children character dolls, were purchased several years ago at a N.A.M.E. Houseparty. They were by an artist only identified as a "sweet little old lady from San Francisco", and sold by Mitzi Gotscher. They are ¼ " scale and much sought after by miniature collectors. The author feels fortunate to have acquired these, since they are no longer being offered thru either Ms. Gotscher or another agent. Seated in front of the brass trunk, is a Vienna bronze figure w/lap-dog; atop the trunk is jointed porcelain doll, now being reproduced. Lying in foreground, is Cecil Boyd's new-born baby, (see *Color Plate 9*). Note the natural curvature of its tiny arches and toes.
The stunning all-brass trunk with copper hardware, is an identical copy of a full-sized trunk owned by Stephen Goode, who made this counterpart with all handmade parts, including hinges, corners, latch, etc. All parts are workable, and the interior of the trunk is completely finished "ready for travel". It certainly is the kind of trunk a miniaturist would not wish to store in an attic, but rather use as a showpiece!
Photo: Dave Hammell; All pieces except brass trunk, from Author's Collection

COLOR PLATE 9
The master bedroom of THE VANE EAGLE mansion, has been rearranged
to afford the reader a better view of the frilly bedclothes designed and made
by the author by selecting the smallest design from eight different styles of
imported lace and satin ribbons. Embroidered rosebuds were added by the
author to carry out wallpaper motif. Bedclothes are all handsewn, then custom-
fitted to the Victorian bedstead. The matching dresser chest with mirror, has
been moved to the rear of room where the bed ordinarily is placed. The young
mother of this household is represented by a most versatile figure made by
Cecil Boyd. (See Cover) The infant drawing her absorbed and loving glance,
is also by Cecil Boyd, (Masterpiece Museum Miniatures). Baby's name is Boyd.
The ceiling light and lamps provide a soft mood to the lovely scene. Pincushion
doll, completely handmade, sewn, and handpainted, is by Susan Hendrix. On
the satin covered boudoir chair is a blue corset by Susan's daughter, Shirlee
Pierce. Baby bassinette, by Clare Albert, is shown in all its loveliness on *Color
Plate 16*. On the Victorian dresser, is a vanity set comprised of 15 molded plastic
pieces which the author has handpainted and glazed to represent Limoges china.
The clock has a handpainted dial, custom-cut and fitted into the oval by the
author; to the left is a pastel portrait made to resemble the figure on the bed.
A ball-fringe and lace suggests curtains, but the windows are left uncovered,
providing a different angle from outside looking in. Red roses in bowl were a
Mother's Day gift to author from her daughter. Only one half of the bedroom
can be seen in this picture; the other half incorporates a fireplace with raised
hearth covered in "Delft" tiles, to match the sides and mantle. A highboy can
be seen just behind the bassinette. The "fainting couch" shown on the cover,
and the rocker shown in *Color Plate 17*, have been borrowed from this master
bedroom. Note Barbara Bunce's incredible jewelry! (More on *Plates 2, 81 & 82)*
Photo: Dave Hammell; Author's Collection

COLOR PLATE 10

Except for the different color background, this vignette features 1″:1′ scale miniatures shown on the Cover of this book.

The author's original design for this handpainted rug, was inspired by the carpet in her childhood home. Drawing upon memory, the intervening years have doubtless colored that recollection, thus producing a rather more vivid floor covering than the era would have "tolerated". This carpet is in the entryhall of THE VANE EAGLE.

A meridienne for noonday napping, (often called a "fainting couch"), has appliques of embroidered petitpoint on lace, salvaged from old Victorian parlorwork. The incised patterns and styling suggests that the couch is American "Eastlake". The English bone china thimble, with its handpainted pink rose, picks up the pattern in the petitpoint, as well as providing a sense of scale to the setting.

Busily perusing the fashion page, is the mother figure by Cecil Boyd, (as seen in *Color Plate 9*). The author has named her dollhouse mother, "Melissa Anne".

The petitpoint work on the wood frame, was purchased in Silver Spring, Maryland, and is a one-of-kind offering from one of their local miniaturists.

Miriam Irwin's MOSAIC PRESS produced the luxurious leather-bound and gold embossed book, "Lichens", an elegant little book (15/16″, 48 pages), whose charming text about these hardy, unusual plants, teaches another lesson about the wonders of Nature. (See SOURCES)

The inlaid wood table of splendid design, is the work of Joan and Bill Helton, whose miniature creations have been recently reported in several noteworthy publications. The handblown pitcher and glass filled with "iced tea", and touched with a "slice of lemon", were purchased in a roadside miniature shop outside Pittsfield, Massachusettes. The realistic halved sandwich was bought at Alice's Imagination Shop. The tray belongs to a tea set in the mansion's dining room.

Photo: Dave Hammell; Author's Collection

COLOR PLATE 11

Grandmother Anne Katherine, has donned her hat--securely anchored with a hatpin--and has gone shopping.

The produce stands and crates were made by Bonnie and Stephen Goode, who sell them as pictured, or in kit form. The crates, made from alder wood, have labels which the makers designed themselves, or have been copied from the colorful full-size old-time shipping labels. Some of the crates are actually stamped on the end pieces with a regular small-type stamping machine that Bonnie Goode bought at a "garage sale".

The actual fruits and vegetables packed in colorful array in the produce crates, are made by Bonnie Goode from Fimo or Sculpey modeling compounds. All are listed in the *Many Goode* catalog. (see SOURCES and CATALOGUES) Another maker of fine produce, including a luscious "cantalope", is Kim Burgin of Kims Miniatures, 1002 Cypress St., San Dimas, CA 91773.

Bagged potatoes "in a net", soda-crackers in a barrel, and Grandma holding a head of purple cabbage, all create a realistic hint of Country Store nostalgia.

A silver Roosevelt dime (10 cents), creates a sense of miniature scale to the seemingly eatable watermelon and other "fresh" fruits and vegetables.

Figure: Cecil Boyd, MASTERPIECE MUSEUM MINIATURES, who also made the entreating pup wistfully eyeing the soda-crackers.

Produce counter, shelves, boxes, baskets, and just about everything required to build a Country Store, can be supplied by S.H. Goode & Sons Workshop. (See CATALOGUES)

Photo: Dave Hammell; Author's Collection, unless otherwise noted

COLOR PLATE 12
This is the planned sewing corner for Mrs. Primrose, shown holding a crochet ꜱ?wing basket by Vivian Litsch. The fitted, *open* sewing basket is shown on *Plate 56*.

Seated on the unusual chair (left), is a Vienna bronze kitty w/ball, done in such perfect detail that even the tiny whiskers seem real rather than metallic. The boxwood spools are wound with single strand silk thread; skeins of embroidery yarn are in open drawer; a wooden stocking darner and sewing box containing buttons and other needs, adds to the theme of this charming vignette.

Large dress form and vintage sewing machine are from a Chrysnbon kit put together by Al Baker, then painted by the author. Chair, (with seated figure by Cecil Boyd), is an import from The Republic of China, available from Gim Fong's shop. (See SOURCES) Wood lacquered plate stand by Gim Fong. Chest of drawers made by author's son, George; "Tiffany" table lamp was a N.A.M.E. Houseparty "favor". The smaller dress form, next to the sewing machine, has been "dressed" in an original gown by the author. It is unfinished, and the remaining fabric is on the chest of drawers.

The spool of thread on the sewing machine is actually part of the plastic mold, but it has been painted to give a realistic appearance to match the other wooden spools of actual thread on the sewing machine work area, laden with safety pins, and ivory thimble--all from Bonnie and Stephen Goode collection--lending realism to the make-believe scene. The dress patterns complete the picture. The 1":1' scale hooked rug came from an old miniature dollhouse setting, and a gift to the author from Doris Gaston. The full length mirror has been borrowed from THE VANE EAGLE master bedroom. The wallpaper pattern has been put up in the horizontal, although the pattern is printed in the vertical. This gives spaciousness and wider breadth to a small area.
Photo: Dave Hammell; Author's Collection, unless otherwise noted

COLOR PLATE 13

Grandmother Anne Katherine is preparing to leave a dish of cookies next to the glass of milk. This is for Santa. Her beautiful beads and earrings are by Barbara Bunce. Lighted chandelier is a kit. Author has gilded the frame and painted the plastic prisms with an iridescent paint so they appear to be genuine finely cut crystal.

The dining room set is made by Reminiscence in Miniature, purchased from Alice's Imagination Shop. The marble topped sideboard has a tilted "petticoat mirror", a special aid for the hostess and her female guests. The pewter tray is shown in more detail on the Cover of this book. The ruby and cobalt blue stemware are from a set of 6 which are ordinarily on display on the wide sill at the opposite end of this room. (The high window with this glass display can be seen from the exterior on *Plate 45*)

The superb example of mini-needlepoint craft is exhibited under the dining room table. It is the work of Renee Marshall, who made it from a kit especially for the author. The decorative plant on wooden display stand, atop the corner china cabinet, is by Gim Fong who carved and lacquered the adjustable plate stand.

Blown glass punchbowl w/ladel and cups, is from Alice's Imagination Shop. Red linen napkins w/rings, are from Lynne's Miniature Treasures catalog.

Susan Hendrix made the tempting assortment of traditional Christmas candies on a plate. Wall sconce with double candelabra, crystal drops, and mirror, were purchased at N.A.M.E. 1982 Houseparty.

A glimpse of a silver punchbowl on drop-leaf table, set under window (rear), can be seen more fully on *Plate 48.*

The open-work curtains, which permit a viewer to gaze into the dining room from the front of the house, thus affording a completely different perspective, were cut from a laundry bag made especially for fine "undies". The pattern is a splendid 1/12" version of the authentic "lace" or "tatted" curtains of yesteryear.

The painted door-frame, matched in color to the wallpaper print, opens to the entryhall, and is directly across from the parlor door. The "fretwork" is another improvisation, which provides an individual touch to the mansion. The author used the "zig-zag" of a plastic chignon comb, glued it in its stretched position against the door frame, then covered the join with a slim trim of decorative wood. Once painted, the entire piece appears to be of custom-cut wood. A little bit of ingenuity will halt big inroads into the budget.

Photo: Dave Hammell; Author's Collection

COLOR PLATE 14

The parlor furniture in THE VANE EAGLE has been rearranged to give a better vantage to the viewer. The Victorian sofa, uphostered in red, has been moved aside to reveal a chess game in progress. A pair of William and Mary side chairs are normally at each end of the playing table. These chairs and the Queen Anne Bookcase (left wall), are from the Stuart Library collection, made by Goebel. (See SOURCES) Also from this collection is the Charles II Armchair, shown between the coal burning stove and the parlor organ. The stove with "burning embers", has been electrified, as are the lamps which can be seen lighted in the hanging fixture and atop the organ.

The Victorian parlor stove appears to be a replica of the one made by Cribben & Sexton Co., Chicago, Illinois ca. 1880. It was of cast iron, nickle plated decoration, and many had a copper finial. This miniature replica is fine quality molded plastic, fully assembled when purchased. The stovepipe leads into an existing fireplace that has been "boarded up", although the ornate Victorian mantle has remained as a reminder of this "modernization" from wood to coal. Tempting packages by Cynthia Herrmann. The hanging Victorian parlor lamp was a kit made of silver color pot metal; it was enamelled by the author.

Two Vienna bronzes--a kitty and a dachshund on a pillow--keep the master of the house company. A Cecil Boyd MASTERPIECE MUSEUM MINIATURE figure, this piece was custom ordered by the author, and was originally the young lad in short pants on *Plate 14.* Husband and father of this happy household, has been named "Franklin" by the author. No surname has been given the family because it represents *any* American family of the Victorian-Edwardian era of rapid and exciting changes and innovations--moral and material.

Against the far wall is a combination bookcase/secretary desk. The curios displayed alongside the books in each glassed cabinet, are primarily pre-1930 mini collectibles. Painting above secretary is an original miniature watercolor, ca. 1900, from the author's collection. Above the organ is a flower print in a Baroque Frame, one of the accessory pieces in The Stuart Library collection.

Organ from *Lynne's Miniature Treasures* catalog, has been hand decorated by the author; white roses in brass bowl on table under sill, is from Bonnie Goode's collection, purchased from La Petit Fleur, a mini-maker who sells her unique handmade wares at N.A.M.E. Houseparties. Next to this floral display, is an antique handcarved wooden sculpture (maker unknown).

The fabulous caned chair, is a copyright (1979) design, made in U.S.A. for Malcolm Thomas, initialed "D.F." on underside. Author purchased this at an antique show in Pasadena. This gem is found in the entryway, where it serves as companion piece to an oak bookcase/secretary set in the rear portion of the hall. (See *Plate 57)*

Photo: Dave Hammell; Author's Collection, unless otherwise noted

COLOR PLATE 15

Were it not for the common household straight pin shown on the bottom shelf, the items on this page might well fool the observer into concluding they were full size antiques and collectibles from the Victorian-Edwardian era. These highly-prized miniature dollhouse accessories are in the author's collecton, and they provide rare touches of authenticity when properly placed in THE VANE EAGLE mansion.

TOP ROW, (Left to Right); A lady's chapeau very much in keeping with a "Sunday Best", or "Easter Bonnet" fashion accessory ca. 1918. (Gift to the author from Zaney Erchul, on the occasion of the first International Convention for Collectors of Hatpins and Hatpin Holders. This organization, ICC of H&HH, was founded by the author in August 1977, following the publication of the first definitive world-wide encyclopedia on the subject of hatpins and hatpin holders. *Hatpins & Hatpin Holders: An Illustrated Value Guide*, is a 1983 supplemental work, published by Collector Books, Paducah, KY.) Appropiately placed next to the hat, is a vanity set handcrafted and painted by ceramist Norma Johnston. The "hatpins" are round-headed shirt pins, with heads painted by the author. On the tray are the toilette accessories: hair receiver, powder box, hatpin holder, and a 3/16″ ruby glass teeniest of baskets, with woven spun glass and clear glass applied handle. The gold "mesh" purse w/ornate silver frame, clasp and chain, is one of several dozen made by N.A.M.E. Houseparty Helpers as "favors" at the 1982 successful Convention. The crochet pair of gloves, were made by Faye Hatfield, Irving, Texas.

CENTER, (Left to Right): 5/16″ overall length, this artglass handmade wee bird has incredible detail. American glassblowers produced beautiful art glass in Sandwich, Mass., Wheeling, West Virginia, and in Pennsylvania and Ohio glassmaking centers. Iridescent glass, cobalt, and threaded or ribbon glass was blown into charming miniature replicas, such as pictured on center and bottom rows. All have pontils except the amber and green free-form vase with applied base. The tiny elephant with trunk in the air, is carmel slag. ca. 1900. These fine examples of ingenious glassmaking were originally housed in an antique dollhouse. When the dollhouse and its contents were offered for sale, along with a vast collection of other miniaturia, the author had the happy good fortune of acquiring several of these pieces from the new owner. The three pieces on the middle shelf, are mementoes given the author by Milly Combs as special "housewarming gifts" to commemorate the first "open house" for visitors to THE VANE EAGLE mansion in miniature.

Photo: Dave Hammell; Author's Collection

COLOR PLATE 16
Pieces that provide interest and a feeling of luxury or opulence to a Victorian home, are shown here in a mock setting.
Left to Right:
    Rose satin covered boudoir chair, shown in *Color Plate 9*, was acquired at Alice's Imagination Shop.
    The bassinette, fit for a baby princess, was handmade by Clare Albert from the original design and patterns created by LaNeva Peacock of Mox Nix. (See SOURCES) Mrs. Peacock teaches classes in miniature-making, does specialized custom work, and is a masterful pattern maker in addition to supplying the materials in her step-by-step mini-productions. In addition to classes in her shop, she expects her "students" to do "homework" on the current group project. It was with LaNeva's clearly outlined instructions, that Clare Albert was able and encouraged to create this precious Victorian style baby-bed for the newly born pride of the household. The bassinette is shown in *Color Plate 9*, in its rightful place, the master bedroom.
    Propped against the fanciful crib, is Georgia Luna Villalobos' 1/12″ scaled "Bye-lo Baby", ca. 1923. This doll was packaged in individual boxes labelled, *"The Almost Human Doll"*.
    Villalobos' miniature model of the "Bye-lo Baby", measures 2″ head to toe; dressed in baptismal gown, the baby has a 3½″ overall dimension. (See TINY TALES, about this mini-master) The *mini*-"Bye-lo Baby" is available at all stores selling choice miniatures, or from Allin R. Yarwood Enterprises who features the doll at the California Gift Shows.
    The Oriental style table, from the collection of Milly Combs, was made by Bill Helton. (See SOURCES) The figurine of a little girl w/doll, is a "Staffordshire" piece from England; the white porcelain Lotus bowl was purchased from Gim Fong. (See SOURCES) Another Helton uniquely designed and hand-crafted table, provides a stand for the silver-overlay cobalt blue vase w/handmade roses, (one of a pair), given as a gift to the author from a longtime friend. They are appropriately shown on either side of the fireplace mantle on *Color Plate 14*. Lying on the seat of the rare antique hand-carved chair, is a Vienna bronze dachshund on pillow, as seen on *Color Plate 14*. This beautiful chair, with its "chippendale" work, is utilized as a desk chair in the Victorian parlor where its rather baroque styling would be appropriate to its surroundings. This old piece of dollhouse furniture, originally in a turn-of-the-century miniature mansion, was a gift to the author from Ginny Olson.
    The "needlepoint" area rug, which is ordinarily alongside the Victorian bedstead in the master bedroom of THE VANE EAGLE, is an original design and handpainted by the author who tried to achieve the look of a needlepoint rug by using the impressionist-painter's "dots" instead of brush strokes. Fringe on this and other rugs in the dollhouse, were hand-pulled from a fine cotton broadcloth, then pasted to the underside edges of the rug.
    Photo: Dave Hammell; Author's Collection, unless otherwise noted

COLOR PLATE 17
THE VANE EAGLE miniature study/library, is one of the author's favorite rooms in the mansion.
   Against lefthand wall is an Oriental ginger jar, a gift to the author from her daughter. The fine porcelain is a product of Titania Pottery, signed by the ceramist, J. Angelus de Conta, who also did the delicate handpainting.
   The combination bookcase/Secretary-desk, is a commercial kit by House of Miniatures, (See SOURCES), put together with painstaking care by the author's son, and given several coats of finish and treatment accorded any fine antique period piece. Atop the bookcase, is a boat-in-a-bottle. The *Victrola* record player was purchased at Alice's Imagination Shop, as a Christmas gift from author's husband. A music sheet with "His Master's Voice" trademark was reduced until the round disc was scaled to mini-size. The man of the house, obviously a music lover, is reclining on a rocker made by Clare Albert, from a design by LaNeva Peacock. The matching footstool acts as a prop for the Marilyn Worth masterful violin and bow. (See *Plate 8* for detail work required for this musical instrument.)
   A glimpse of the stone fireplace can be seen on the right side wall, with its heavy wood mantle which is crowded with memorabilia "collected" by the male figure named "Franklin", by the author. The figure is by Cecil Boyd, MASTERPIECE MUSEUM MINIATURES. (See SOURCES)
   The Victorian Wall Clock was acquired from Alice's Imagination Shop, at a N.A.M.E. Houseparty, attended by Alice who, as with many other fine dealers, makers, and hobbyists, features a variety of exciting miniatures available for sale. The table under the window sill, is Bill Helton's work, and is shown on the Cover of this book. The table is laden with a brass kerosene lamp that has been "converted" to electricity. This lamp *lights*, as does the ceiling fixture which has been gilded by the author, converting it from a drab silver metal to a more vibrant tone in keeping with the warmth of the room.
   Through the windowpane, one can see the "wrought iron" work and the railing of the upstairs balcony. The potted plants, all made of wood (German), are on a wicker table. Inside, on the table under the window, is a rare one-of-a-kind *plique-a-jour* enamel bowl on a hand-carved wood display stand. The bowl is from the private collection of Gim Fong, who is also the artisan. (See TINY TALES Section). It was loaned to the author expressly for this book, and according to all reports, Gim Fong is the only maker of *miniature 1":1' plique-a-jour* and *cloisonne* artifacts world-wide. The exhibit of his work, (not for sale), is a highlight of any visit to his shop. Mr. Fong also made the wood plate stand which displays a lovely porcelain plate purchased by the author at a miniature show. On the fireplace mantle, a rider on horseback follows the same theme as on the plate, and on the wall is still another example of an equestrian motif. The small wallshelf is one of a pair. A handpainted metallic figure of a Chinese peasant woman, is shown on this Plate; the other, on a section of the room not shown, is the mate--a Chinese male in "Coolie" or Mandarin-style hat. Alongside the lead soldier on a horse, is a scaled 1":1' crystalized geode, and if one looks carefully, there's a tiny glimpse of a Christmas decoration. The latter is shown in full on *Color Plate 6*, atop the mantle.
Photo: Dave Hammell; Author's Collection, unless otherwise noted

COLOR PLATE 18

A perfect vehicle for Clare Albert's promethean efforts, is her Victorian dollhouse bed, all of pink silk and white lace. Designed by LaNeva Peacock, Clare utilized patterns and step-by-step instructions provided by LaNeva, and in approximately 30 hours of meticulous work was able to achieve stunning results. (See MOX NIX under SOURCES) The commercially made bedstead was purchased ready-made, but was taken completely apart and rebuilt to make it appear higher and more "comfortable" than most mass-produced miniature beds. The top of the tester (canopy), is tufted; the backboard is covered with pink silk with "Austrian Drapes", or "sheers" carefully sewn in traditional design. Five different fragile laces were hand sewn, as was the perfect pleating in the dust-ruffle.

The headboard with canopy is 8"H x 5"W; the quilted tester or hood measures 3¼" at its widest point, and is trimmed with 1" lace.

The bed has 4" bed-posts, and measures 4½"W x 6½"L x 2¼"H, including the 1" pleated dust-ruffle.

The beautiful headboard has side curtains which are drawn back on each side, and are held securely in place by miniature white silk cord tie-backs. The graceful dip of the folds is acquired by the artful tug of those cords which were placed and used to best advantage, thus giving a look of grace to the entire project.

This enchanting piece is the owner's favorite, and any dollhouse bedroom planned around this bed would be inspired by this masterful creation.

Photo: Dave Hammell; Clare Albert Collection

COLOR PLATE 19

Miniature cabinet pieces are usually not made with precision scaling in mind, but rather answer the challenge of making "little things" that appeal to the sensitive and sentimental side of collectors. Nevertheless, the techniques used and the extraordinary demand for exactitude, have made cabinet or display miniatures favored by those people not catagorized as collectors but who, nevertheless, have purchased miniature pieces merely out of admiration for exceptional curios. They are not necessarily dollhouse enthusiasts or miniaturists, *per se*, but have a distinct appreciation for works of artistic merit, of which small cabinet *objet d'art* fully qualify. Many of these curios are museum pieces, well out of reach of the ordinary collector or admirer; still, there are works of mini-makers which are readily collectible in ones travels, and dozens of examples may be found as souvenirs saved from yesteryear. A large percentage of these cabinet pieces are now accomodated in room-boxes and dollhouses, especially when the object is reasonably scaled to size.

TOP SHELF: ¾" handwrought brass pitcher with copper wire overlay; 1" handcarved wooden piece depicting a young girl holding a large straw hat w/streamers; 1½" handcarved wooden piece, a woman in peasant dress leaning on a staff. (Unknown maker, ca. 1930)

MIDDLE: A Vienna bronze Dachshund with her two pups, measuring an incredible 1" from tip of nose to curled tail. These highly collectible Vienna bronzes are steadily bringing higher prices; a 2" Vienna bronze Hare, boasting ½" laid-back ears, and a Pussywillow branch in mouth plus an egg-shaped polished chalcedony stone, suggests the coming of Spring and Eastertime. The detail shown in the metallic engraving of the Hare, may be compared to the familiar woodcut, "The Hare", by Durer. Next is a 1" Vienna bronze rabbit w/basket, in red coat.

BOTTOM: Handpainted 2" bisque figures, Indian motif, with "Germany" incised mark, ca. 1930; 7/8" diameter handwoven basket with lid, made of horse hair, crafted by the Papago Indians on their Arizona reservation. The automobile trunk key, measuring 1¾", dwarfs the basket, and emphasizes the immense skill required in weaving the design and cylindrical shape of the basket which is unique to this Indian tribe. Although miniature basket weaving was begun in ancestral times, it has continued to flourish even as late as the sixties, when the basket pictured herein was purchased through a Papago Indian Self-Help Program facility on the reservation. The basket was made by Alice Miguel Ventana. Papago baskets are made by sewing coils together; these coils are either of bear-grass or horse hair. The secondary coil is wound around the primary coil and is stitched through the preceding coil to hold the basket together. The white coils are of bleached yucca leaf or of willow shoots; the green is unbleached yucca leaf; the brown is yucca root; the black is of devil's claw seed pod. Infinite patience and distinct sense of design are the necessary traits to produce such peerless, novel miniatures.

Photo: Dave Hammell; Barbara Lee Hammell Collection

COLOR PLATE 20
Pretty as a picture that could be mounted on a wall, is the 6½″ x 8″ needle-punch rug made from a commercial kit by Clare Albert for her miniature house.
Clare estimates that it took her a minimum of eight hours to accomplish this highly creative carpet which would enhance any mini-setting.
Photo: Dave Hammell; Clare Albert Collection

COLOR PLATE 21
Through the open back of THE VANE EAGLE mansion, we can see the upstairs bathroom which includes the dainty patterned wallpaper and luxurious blue porcelain fixtures.

The window has a drawn windowshade over translucent glass pane, (for privacy). The modest little girl in her tub is a porcelain collectible, "Sudsi Suzie", by The McClellands, an exclusive edition by RECO Collection. This was purchased at Eva Marie Dry Grocer, Redondo Beach, California, which is a novel showplace for many collectibles.

Author handpainted the child's potty and bathroom stool. Note electrified lamp over sink, installed by R.A. Baker.

Small rugs in background were made by Virginia McCurdy as a gift to author. Large rug in foreground is 3¾″ x 5¾″ on Navy #18 gauge Hardanger from a Grigg pattern. However, the color scheme is an original concept by maker, Clare Albert, who made this rug to match the color scheme in her own miniature house.

The "widow's walk" and dual chimney are seen from back of THE VANE EAGLE mansion.

Many accessories may be seen on the cabinet, such as an old fashioned razor w/strop hanging close by, a drinking glass, and other bathroom necessities.

Photo: Dave Hammell; Author's Collection except for large rug from Clare Albert's Collection.

COLOR PLATE 22

Another view of the Master Bedroom in THE VANE EAGLE miniature mansion, showing the fireplace and display wall designed by the author and built by R.A. Baker.

The "Dutch Tiles" are actually printed paper which has been pasted on to a wood frame to give the impression of a raised hearth and tiled fireplace.

The fireplace's and-irons are the top half of turned spindles; the lower half of the and-irons are from excess wood cutouts. All wood pieces were gilded to appear metallic.

The beautiful boudoir chair with slipper satin upholstery, was manufactured by Fantastic Merchandise, a company that supplies many mini-shops. A detailed picture of this chair is on *Color Plate 16.*

The rugs in this room were designed and handpainted by the author. Upon the tall chest in rear, is a glass tray with perfume bottles and atomizer made by the talented Susan Hendrix of Fallbrook, California.

The "Staffordshire" china figurine on center of fireplace and on rear chest are from the Steak Family Miniatures, Newport Beach, California.

The replica 1″ scale Stafforshire china dogs on the hearth were purchased at auction and were originally in a dollhouse ca. 1925, as was the tall Oriental vase which is handpainted.

The bedroom door and the doors throughout the house, were designed by the author.

Gold fringe at top of windows is to suggest draperies and/or curtains, but the windows of the mansion are left uncovered for better viewing at various angles. This also offered a unique challenge to the author to decorate from corner to corner, rather than merely from a "back-view" into a room.

The full size bed and other view of this bedroom may be seen on *Color Plate 9.*

The ceiling lighted fixture and wallpaper was finely executed by R.A. Baker.

Photo: Dave Hammell; Author's Collection

COLOR PLATE 23
Another view of the dining room in THE VANE EAGLE, showing the high window which displays prized wine goblets and other collectible miniature glass, including the vaseline glass vase from "Glass Concepts", an Illinois based company that sells to mini-shops.

The claw-footed "Grand Rapids" golden oak dining table with four golden oak plush-covered chairs, are by Fantastic Merchandise, makers of fine miniatures for distribution by mini-shops.

The large platter and porcelain pieces in the corner cabinet are marked "Limoge, France".

The Oriental clay figure with fan, atop the corner cabinet, is from an old collection of Oriental miniature figures, ca. 1930.

An outside view of this high window can be seen on *Plate 45*. The beginnings of this dining room can be seen on *Plate 43*.

Window treatment conceived and built by the author.
Photo: Dave Hammell; Author's Collection

COLOR PLATE 24
Two of a set of four dining room chairs all cut, shaped, and carved by Clare Albert, using a Dremel Moto-tool. Simulated caning was achieved by using needlepoint canvas. Padded seats are counted cross-stitch w/multi-color floral centers. Patterns for the chairs and table (not shown), are by LaNeva Peacock, Mox Nix Shop, Metairie, LA (See SOURCES). The Firescreen is counted cross-stitch on #22 count Hardanger. Frame was custom built and then mounted on a commercially purchased frame. Measurements: Approx. 4″ height overall; frame 1½″ x 1½″. All mahogany wood. Rug: 4″ x 6″, counted cross-stitch on #14 Aida Cloth, from a June Grigg design. All handiwork by Clare Albert.
Photo: Dave Hammell; Clare Albert Collection

Photographs

Plates 62-85

PLATE 62
TOP, Left to Right;
Handpainted porcelain dolls in typical Dutch costume; wee china Teddy; Teddy Bear Cookie Jar (one shown with cover removed); handpainted Staffordshire Tea Pot.
CENTER, Left to Right;
Scaled dollhouse Kewpies; metal-jointed Teddy & Bunny; porcelain Tea Set, handpainted.
BOTTOM, Left to Right;
Walnut chest w/"silverware"; *Salt, Tea, Coffee* advertising tins; walnut chest w/duelling pistols (shown with open and closed lid).
Photo: Paul Highfill; Patti & Paul Highfill Collection

PLATE 63
Assortment of wood, metal, and porcelain clocks for the mantle, wall, and decorative decor. All by Patti Highfill. (See SOURCES)
Photo: Paul Highfill; Patti & Paul Highfill Collection

PLATE 64

PLATE 65

PLATES 64, 65, 66
Above Victorian "Santa" Candy Box, displayed by owner, Patti Highfill. Note size of Santa's hand holding the Christmas tree, and Patti's touching Santa's old-fashion hood. *Plate 65* affords appreciation of full detail. *Below* An exhibit of handpainted Staffordshire-type "Scent Houses", (Victorian incense burners), handmade in "Sculpy" by Patti Highfill. No two are exactly alike. A perfect touch for the Victorian parlor.
Photos: Dale Fink; Patti & Paul Highfill Collection

PLATE 66

PLATE 67
Patti Highfill's original porcelain doll which she has dressed in a micro-crochet outfit. The layette ensemble consists of carriage shawl w/pillow; *saque*, bonnet and booties. The baby, dressed in Christening gown and bonnet, with lace slip and diaper. (See SOURCES)
Photo: Dale Fink; Patti & Paul Highfill Collection

PLATE 68
Victorian painted and lacquered wooden sewing boxes, and open sewing baskets, both fully equipped, are more of the ingenious handiwork of Patti Highfill. Full-size thimble provides reader with quality of miniaturization undertaken by this mini-master.
Photo:Paul Highfill; Patti & Paul Highfill Collection

BEAUTIFUL PACKAGES are expertly wrapped by Cynthia Herrmann, and are only sold through specialty shops and at miniature shows. A list of these sources can be obtained by sending a SASE to Cynthia Herrmann, 1749 So. Shenandoah St., Los Angeles, CA 90035.

PLATE 69
TOP ROW, Left to Right; ¾″ long x ¼″ wide, by 1 1/8″ tall, complete with ribbon and tag, is the tallest package; BOTTOM ROW, next to 25 cents coin, is teeny package only 7/16″ x ¼″ x 5/8″. All paper is scaled for mini-use as are the bright satin bows.
Photo: Courtesy Cynthia Herrmann

PLATE 70
Foil and various textures of paper, and special little holiday accents, add to the special charm of Cynthia's packaging. Note the wee gift-tags. Several Christmas-wrapped packages, made by Cynthia Herrmann, are in the author's collection. See them in *full color* on *Color Plates 6, 7, & 14.*
Photo: Courtesy Cynthia Herrmann

CUSTOM MINIATURES by A. Thomay are featured on Plates 71 thru 77. (See TINY TALES section, and SOURCES)

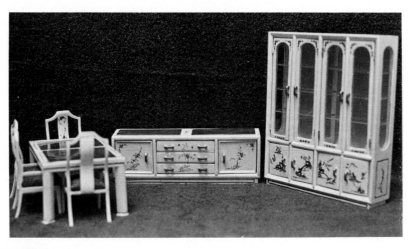

PLATE 71
Mandarin Dining Room Group includes 3½″W x 7″H x 1½″D China Cabinet. Upper section's two doors have Plexiglas; interior fitted with two Plexi shelves; lower section's two doors have beveled wood inserts. *Chinoiserie* decoration.
Photo: Courtesy A. Thomay

PLATE 72
Oriental Angled China Cabinet, size 5 3/8″W x 6¾″H x 1¼″D. All handcrafted, w/Plexiglas openings and shelves. Doors and drawers open; finest detailing *Chinoiserie* fashion.
Photo: Courtesy A. Thomay

PLATE 73
Magnificently black-lacquered hardwood *Amoire,* with two drawers and two inside shelves, fully finished. All-over dimension: 6¼"H x 4¼"W x 2"D. Exquisite miniature paintings in *Chinoiserie* style.
Photo: Courtesy A. Thomay

PLATE 74
Mandarin Buffet Beveled Cabinet w/Side Chairs. Buffet top boasts Carpathian burl-wood inlay; size, 7½"W x 2½"H x 1½"D. Handcrafted pulls on doors and drawers which are operable. Custom upholstered seats are sewed in fabrics that are selected to complement the color of the lacquer used. Note curvature of back rests, and intricate handwork & painting.
Photo: Courtesy A. Thomay

PLATE 75
Cathay Bedroom Suite, consists of an *Amoire,* Night Stand, Upholstered headboard (complete with foam mattress and bed frame), Mirror in hardwood frame
above a 9-drawer Dresser. Black lacquered hardwoods in Oriental design,
highlighted with artful *Chinoiserie* patterns. A. Thomay's exceptional pieces
are merchandised in Palm Beach, Florida; also by direct catalogue sales. (See
CATALOGUES)
Photo: Courtesy A. Thomay

PLATE 76
A close-up photo of the Dresser, part of the Cathay Bedroom Suite shown on
Plate 75, emphasizes the exceptional attention paid to detailing on this and
all A. Thomay's Oriental miniature pieces. This dresser is 1/12" scale: 6¾"W
x 2 7/8"H, x 1 7/8"D.
Photo: Courtesy A. Thomay, from his collection

PLATE 77
Breakfront of magnificent design and craftsmanship, all hand-crafted and painted in *Chinoiserie* style. An exciting miniature masterpiece, measuring 9¾"W x 7½"H x 1½"D, this piece represents almost 150 hours of work. *Photo: Courtesy A. Thomay, from his collection*

PLATE 78
Dry sink is from a commercial kit manufactured by "Scientific Realife". Grinder, molds, and other accessories inside sink are available through mini-catalogues or mini-shops. Ice cream churn and bucket are from Lynne's Miniature Treasures catalogue. Blown glass preserve jar was made by "Miniature Glass Parts," owned by Don Winters, mini-artisan from California.
Photo: Dave Hammell; Author's Collection

PLATE 79
Fireplace for Mrs. Primrose's bedroom, designed by the author using "leftovers" from the mansion project. Hearth rug with Eagle design, was painted by the author with colored felt-tipped pens. Cotton fringe and cardboard backing. Hearth brick is a paper-print design. Exquisite "Dresden" figurine is from Steak Family Miniatures, (Francis Steak, Newport Beach, California), offering commercial sales at N.A.M.E. Houseparties. The figurine decorative "stand" is actually a gilded picture frame with opening covered by the base of figurine. Highly detailed figurine is fine bone china, and handpainted. Pair of oval 1 3/8″ x 1¾″ counted crosstitch pictures are by Clare Albert from her collection of fine needlecraft. Floral patterns are charted designs by June Grigg's *Charted Designs for Miniatures*, copyright 1979 by June Grigg Designs Atlanta, P.O. Box 88224, Atlanta, GA 30338.
Photo: Dave Hammell; Author's collection unless otherwise noted

PLATE 80
Author re-designed a commercial kit for a canopy bed, and converted it into Mrs. Primrose's sleeping accomodation. Turned spindles with a small bead on top, and beading on top of headboard, gives the appearance of a "spool bed". These same turned spindles, cut to size, were utilized in another fashion on *Color Plate 22*. Wool crochet afghan was won as a door-prize and was hand made by a talented mini-artist from Lawndale, California. The panting hound-dog, made of "Sculpey" and handpainted, is by *Margene* who sells her whimsical creations at mini-fairs and N.A.M.E. conventions.
Photo: Dave Hammell; Author's collection

PLATE 81

"Juliette caps" have popped in and out of style in many periods of fashion history. The last revival was during the "Roaring Twenties", when beaded drops were added to give the cap an Egyptian or Art Deco look. The jewelled caps by Barbara Bunce are scaled 1":1'. For the fairytale setting, what better mood-piece than a King's Crown, complete with "ermine" and status jewels. The *faux* fur trim, even to the ermine tails, gives an authentic look to the overall creation. Barbara Bunce, master miniature jeweler, makes one-of-a-kind delights such as the pieces shown on this page, and on *Plates 2 and 82.*
Photos: Carl Heidel; Barbara Bunce Collection

PLATE 82
Pearls, Jet, Jade, Coral, and Crystals comprise the various matched sets of jewelry by Barbara Bunce. Each set or individual piece, is carefully boxed so the jewelry can either be displayed as a collectible showpiece, or worn by a dollhouse figure. The pieces are unique, individually handmade jewels by a one-of-a-kind jeweler.
Photos: Carl Heidel; Barbara Bunce Collection; (See SOURCES)

PLATE 83
Vignette by the author featuring the versatile male figure created by Cecil Boyd, (Masterpiece Museum Miniatures). The personality completely changes when this figure is placed into another setting, such as shown on *Color Plates 14 and 17.* Puppy is pewter; box "Kodak" w/film by Susan Hendrix & Shirlee Pierce, mother/daughter team of talented miniaturists. Director's Chair, by Allen and Bernice Rice, and Louis Kummerow's tripod camera, were N.A.M.E.Houseparty "favors", California 1982.
Photo: Dave Hammell; Author's Collection

PLATE 84
On the occasion of the author's 25th Wedding Anniversary, the Bakers posed in "old-tyme" wedding costumes for a souvenir picture to be given to son and daughter. The following Christmas, the daughter played Santa to the hilt by having the studio portrait miniaturized 1″:1′ scale, then framed in this ornate gilded period piece which is prominently displayed in the dollhouse master bedroom.
Photo: Dave Hammell; Author's Collection

PLATE 85
A 1″:1′ scale replica of the Englel Feitknecht studio model camera, ca. 1900.
Standing 5½″ tall overall, this extraordinary miniature camera is constructed
of rosewood, satinwood, and cherrywood, all with hand-rubbed oil finish. All
fittings are solid brass. The rear view plate is of frosted glass; the lens is an
F4 glass lens ground to scale-size. By using the brass negative carrier, (made
especially for this camera), the remarkable instrument is actually capable of
taking a picture. The camera, painstakingly made by artist Gary Utz, took
several months to complete. Mr. Utz is a computer engineer from Bellefonte,
Pennsylvania.
Photo: Leonard Nadel; Evelyn DeWolf Nadel Collection

Tips, Sources, People, Publications, Prices

TIDBITS OF HELPFUL TIPS

A handy gadget for metallic pieces: purchase a Hide-a-Key. Pack florist clay or plaster-of-Paris inside the compartment reserved for the spare key. This acts as a weight. Slide cover to close and turn over so the magnet is face-up. Place metallic mini-parts on to magnet; the weight will keep the gadget from sliding.

An easy way to work with white glue: purchase the very smallest available embroidery hoop. Measure off enough wax paper to fit between the hoops. Close the hoops. Pour small quantities in center of wax paper. Replenish as needed. Discard wax paper each day by releasing from the hoops. Easiest cleanup there is!

Need information about current sources or hard-to-find miniatures? Send your requests to *The Private Eye*, PO Box 333, Corona del Mar, CA 92625-0333. Sarah Salisbury, "The Private Eye," is one of many bonus benefits to subscribers of NUTSHELL NEWS. A wealth of information for mini-makers and collectors!

See-through dustcovers for dollhouse: measure dimensions of open-back of dollhouse. Make a pattern on brown wrapping paper. Cut out the pattern and place it against the back of the dollhouse to be sure it fits perfectly. Using thin strips of molding, form an outline of the outside dimensions of the pattern. Next, lay the pattern on clear plastic available in building materials department of most large chain stores. Cut pattern and staple to strips of molding. Drive a 1″ slender nail through each top corner of the molding. Drill a tiny hole at top of each side of back of dollhouse, to allow the nails to set securely into these holes, thus hanging a transparent "shade" over the opening of the dollhouse. A small dab of wax at the bottom corners, will anchor the dustcover in place.

For permanent pleating: hairspray or spray-starch, lightly sprayed and allowed to dry thoroughly, will do the trick.

For rounding and custom-shaping wooden forms: various grades of "roughness" can be found in nail files and Emery boards. These are smaller and easier to use than sandpaper bits and pieces.

Make original designer patterns: Photostat reduction and copy machines are now available at many stationary stores. To reduce your own designs, 64% and less, usually costs under $1.00. Make your design, or copy it from available stencils. Have the copy reduced to scale, (this may take a _second_ reduction of 64%). For extra ease in laying floors, or wallpapering walls & ceilings, have your copy run off on Avery self-stick sheets of paper.

Travel packs for miniatures: 1) self-seal plastic bags and balls of white cotton are perfect travelling companions. Tiny mini purchases should be wrapped in tissue, placed inside the sandwich-sized self-seal bags. Cotton provides extra protection. When zipping plastic bag closed, DO NOT squeeze out the air. The trapped air acts as an "air cushion" against crushing tiny treasures. Larger self-seal bags can be utilized for larger purchases. 2) for ¼ " scale miniatures, place the piece in center of a large plastic bandage (gauze center), and bring adhesive around to make a secure wrap. Use the metallic box as a storage "trunk" when travelling, and you'll bring all safely home.

Separate plastic pieces and keep them in sight: when working with plastic kits that have teeny pieces, use a plastic divided _utensil_ holder. Fill the knife, fork, spoon, sections with about an inch of water. Plastic pieces will float and the partitions will keep them separated.

To make inexpensive "wood carved" accents: put small beads into the sew-hole of fancy buttons, to close off the holes. Then paint the buttons the desired color. Search for buttons in jars, button-boxes, or purchase inexpensive cards of plastic buttons, which often are more intricately molded and represent various decorative periods of design. The sew-holes can also be filled-in with paint, after the buttons are glued into place.

Dollhouse dusty?: Use a hairdryer for the exterior. Cotton swabs clean mirrors, inside glass bottles, etc.. Dip a Q-Tip swab into glass cleaner, using one side for washing, the dry cotton tip at other end for drying.

Plastic flowers: the stamen of plastic flowers can be used as scaled "buds" on various mini-plants. They can also be painted the desired colors.

Prevent loss: put a molding around your worktable, with 1/8 " raised lip which will keep "things" from rolling off a flat surface. Keep a throw-rug underfoot in your work area. If something drops, it can be shaken loose and found again.

TINY TALES ABOUT THE MINI-MAKERS & MINI-MASTERS IN THIS BOOK

"...And however much you condemn the evil in the world, remember that the world is not all evil; that somewhere children are at play, as you yourself in the old days..."
(*Whatever Else You Do*, Max Ehrmann)

In 1927, Max Ehrmann expressed his longing for happiness in his philosophical poem, "The Desiderata of Happiness." The poet assured us that we "are a child of the universe no less than the trees and the stars," and the reader is awakened to his/her uniqueness.

The twenties were teeming with tireless change in social and economic quarters. In 1922, Dr. Hermann Rorschach--a Swiss psychiatrist--introduced a test in which ink blots were used in determining intellect and emotion in "disturbed" individuals. The author as a child, vividly recalls shaking droplets of bottled ink on to the middle of a sheet of white paper, folding the paper in half, then opening it wide to reveal exciting forms--designs by chance. These frayed ink blots played on strings of imagination: butterflies fluttered deco-designed wings; fairies played fifes and illusory forms took definable shapes.

The ability to carry into adulthood this verve of creative illusion and invention, to transform material nothingness into enterprising castle-building, is surely a most useful plumb for pitting aspirations against monetary limitations. Blot-by-blot, so to speak, a successful miniaturist must submit with stubborn self-will to conceptual impressions and "brain-storms". Remember, in today's world of miniaturia, one can do no wrong!

Micro-mania has produced wondrous scaled objects suitable for period pieces, designer dollhouses, vignettes, and dioramas. The ever-widening "cottage industry" producing myriads of miniaturia, is composed of hundreds of local artisans whose talents are responsible for supplying local shops with the highly prized one-of-a-kind articles and specialties. Unique merchandise can be discovered in ones travels, and each locale has varied offerings for "souvenir hunters" including miniatures which are superior and innovative. Many of these bonuses are found by exploring off the main highway and out-of-the-way places. Upon examination of the photographs within this book, the reader will come upon many such examples, and as often as possible the author has given tips on the sources and prices of these creative and collectible miniatures. Newsletters and Periodicals are the best way to keep up with *current* sources and addresses, as well as availability and true current values. There are sections in this book devoted to these matters plus sources and suppliers for items pictured on the color plates and black & white photos. Further interesting facts are provided in the descriptive text accompanying the photographs.

The mini-makers and mini-masters represented in this book, come from all areas of the United States. Some of their candid letters and verbal comments about themselves, communicate a homespun and simple sincerity which endears the symbol and character of the communication. So as not to lose anything in the translation, the author introduces them to the reader with a minimum of editing, yet an author's allowable maximum of poetic license.

MARY "SKIP" ADAIR - "I don't find myself very interesting, just always interested! I became interested in miniatures because I'm a frustrated interior designer who always wished my husband and I could afford an old San Francisco Italianate Victorian to 'fix up' and live in. When I saw a dollhouse in a magazine, of that design, I figured it might be more realistic financially to decorate in 1/12 scale. My son introduced me to Chrysnbon kits and showed *me* how to put them together-- kind of reversed role from when he was a child. Then my husband decided it might be nice to leave the rush of California business and move to the Missouri Ozarks. But what would I do after I had soaked in all that beauty? To be prepared, I began classes in stained glass and bought a DOLLHOUSE SHELL. But we never moved to the Ozarks. Instead, we moved to the State of Washington where we had dozens of relatives, including our oldest son, his wife, and our three grandchildren. Between my relatives and dressing my collection of antique and 'collectible' dolls, there's not nearly enough time for my dollhouse. I used to paint, but that got side-tracked when miniatures entered my life! My wonderful husband, Jim, is patient with the mess I make most of the time, like when I got up enough nerve to make two little Victorian chairs for the master bedroom and the living room suite, *from scratch*! Then I built an addition to my dollhouse when Jim bought me a beautiful 7-member dollhouse family. The grandparent dolls have to just 'visit', as there's no more room for bedrooms. Even though its taken me four years of working every chance I get, my project will become a legacy for my grandchildren from 'Grandma Skip'. And what fun to participate in your book!"

CLARE ALBERT - "After the helter-skelter of hospitals and surgery rooms, my retirement from nursing and retreat to mini-making was just what I needed. The patience and exacting nature of my previous profession came in good stead in my new-found hobby, which has consumed my interests until a week hardly goes by that I don't attend a mini-class at Mox Nix, my neighborhood miniature and hobby shop. From 1″:1′ scale, I'm now into ½″ scale construction, and even learning about landscaping. One never knows ones own hidden and latent talents until meeting the delightful and rewarding challenges of miniatures. If I were asked to recommend the best tonic for boredom, retaining ones balance and perspective, it would have to be mini-magic in maxi-dosage. It sure works for me!"

CECIL BOYD (MASTERPIECE MUSEUM MINIATURES) - Extensive coverage of Cecil's impressive work is shown elsewhere in the pages of this book, and the accompanying text gives much of her background and philosophy.

JOHN M. & ELLEN KRUCKER BLAUER - (Excerpts from "Profile on the Blauers of the Miniature Mart & Peddlers Shop," by John M. Blauer). Born in San Francisco, December 31, 1926, John M. Blauer has been a collector and creator of miniatures since his early childhood. At the age of 14, he went to work for a theatrical costume house that supplied wardrobe for Grand Opera, stage plays and motion pictures. His interest in miniatures and his fascination and appreciation of superior craftsmanship and microscopic detail come, he says, from his late father, Walter M. Blauer, a watchmaker for 50 years and foreman of the watch department of San Francisco's Shreve and Company. He also attributes his early interest in miniature furniture and household accessories to his mother Etoile Millar Blauer, who often spoke of her extensive collection that was destroyed in the 1906 Earthquake and Fire. Before the recent renaissance in miniature collecting, John had the opportunity to acquire several collections in total, and a few choice pieces from others. The largest collection he purchased was from the widow of the famous songwriter Jack Norworth, whose "Shine on Harvest Moon" and "Take Me Out to the Ball Game" are now American song classics. There were over 10,000 individual pieces in the Norworth Collection. Several newspaper and magazine articles were published about John's collection, and such an interest resulted from these publications that he decided to start a mail order business--the now famous Miniature Mart. In 1966 John started to correspond with a young widow, Ellen Gaines Krucker, who had studied as a pianist for the concert stage and gave it up to become a housewife and mother. After the death of her husband, with two young children to support, she became a church organist and textile weaver. She won several national awards for her weaving and decided to start a mail order business selling weaving materials. Her business, The Peddler's Shop, also carried imported beads and metal jewelry findings which John employed in some of his creations. Ellen, who had created some miniatures for her own collection, started to create commercially for The Miniature Mart. Over the years, John and Ellen's mutual interest blossomed into romance and love. On February 3, 1973, they were married at the Victoria and Albert Wedding Chapel in Carson City, Nevada.

STEPHANIE BLYTHE AND SUSAN SNODGRASS - "Susan and I have been making fairies and dolls in collaboration for about 3 years. We have been using Sylvia Mobley's porcelain heads, hands and feet. But last summer artisan Mobley taught me how to make porcelain dolls and we are now starting to create dolls with my porcelain." Readers will find NUTSHELL NEWS, July 1981 article about Sylvia Mobley and her work with Stephanie Blythe and Susan Snodgrass, truly fascinating and informative. The author is privileged to now own a fragile miniature winged fairy resting on a natural rock fragment of amythest crystal, protected under a glass dome. This was purchased at the 1981 "Roarin' Twenties" N.A.M.E. Houseparty, Anaheim, California. Astute collectors, including the Motts, quickly added the few available pieces offered at that convention to their private treasures.

BARBARA BUNCE - "I'm so fascinated by beads and their history. Hatpins seem to have that same interesting past, and what treasures some seem to be, like a bouquet of wonderful flowers. I'm so pleased I have a copy of your hatpin book; someday I will make miniature hatpins to go with the other jewelry. My green opaque beads are as close in color to jade as I can find, and most rare are the fluted brass and pink-gold metal beads used as spacers. One sees these on beaded purses of the most extravagant type, but there aren't very many loose beads around as tiny and perfectly shaped right down to the diamond cut shape. When I buy beads, such as the pink opaque glass, they drive me up a tree as they are not on strings but are loose in the package. They are also very varied as to size and color within that package, so I have to sort through and choose those most uniform, and then string them as a necklace. I'm always trying new styles and designs to fit a particular period. One of the occupational hazards of my choice of mini-hobby, is missing a transparent glass bead in a section of a necklace and then having to redo it. But it's so satisfying to produce scaled jewelry and to find a media, as you once said, 'not yet worked to death'. It's good to be represented in your book; I look forward to it. As a postcript, let me add that my all-engrossing venture into mini-jewelry production came at a time when such involvement saw me through great personal tragedy. From personal experience I know that one can emerge from this by submerging oneself into a pursuit of perfection, whose rewards are the appreciation of others and the satisfaction of reaching a goal.''

SUE DENNIS - ''The hardest thing in the world to do is to write about oneself! I discovered the world of miniatures in 1974 while shopping at a local craft store in San Diego, and its been love ever since. I bought a house kit (1974), and mind you, that thing still isn't finished! I have a long background in the field of animals: managed the health care department of a large pet store chain; was the head surgical technician for a local veterinarian; bred and showed dogs for 10 years, and am currently breeding Appaloosa horses and exotic birds. The arts and crafts have also been a major part of my life. I've done a lot of drawing, painting, and ceramics, so it stands to reason I'd someday put it all together into one major hobby. I'm adding new breeds of cats and dogs all the time, so the list of pets will always be changing. I sell wholesale as well as retail and guarantee my work. If the customer isn't satisfied with a piece, it can be returned for either a refund or replacement. There's no charge for postage and no extra charge for custom colors. I've done a lot of pets (color-wise that is), from photos. Each pet comes in a white gift box with velveteen lining. I'll be doing more Christmas pieces in the future. It's kind of therapeutic--sometimes I need to get my mind off the pets to 'see them better'.''

GIM FONG - ''I have been making miniature *cloisonne* vases, plates, and art goods for my own mini-shop. These are one-of-a-kind pieces that are not marketed. I have to use special wires, enamels, and develop special techniques and tools to work on such small scaled pieces.''

BONNIE & STEPHEN GOODE - ''Steve and I have been into miniatures and small things most of our lives. I think the 'Cracker Jack' toys got us both started, and never having much room was a good reason to keep to *small* things. When I met Steve, he had moved on from Cracker Jack toys to miniature 'booze' bottles. Later on, we both discovered dollhouse miniatures, and before we knew what had hit us, we were hopelessly captured by the challenge. I must admit we have loved every frustrating minute of it! The Introduction to our book, *Introduction to Woods for Miniature Model Making*, tells a little more about how we got started in the miniature business. (See SUGGESTED BOOKS FOR ADDITIONAL READING)

CYNTHIA HERRMANN - ''I have loved miniatures since I was a child. When I'd play with my dolls and miniatures, I'd wrap dominoes for gifts. I enjoy wrapping large presents, so I thought I would try my hand at miniature ones. I've been doing 3D decoupage for 13 years and it has come in handy for the bears, butterflies, etc., that I cut out to put on my bows. Collecting and making miniatures is a wonderful hobby and I have met so many nice people who share this interest."

PATTI HIGHFILL - Patti's world is centered on the creation of dolls and miniatures, and she's gained professional acclaim from her peers. She fires her own porcelain pieces in her home kiln, and her workshop table is usually laden with her delicate, petite miniatures. Her training as artist and craftswoman came to good stead when the popularity of miniatures and dollhouses begged for talent and imagination such as hers. Using petitpoint crocheting techniques, Patti creates dresses and hats; she sews a variety of doll clothing; she paints everything from doll faces to tole patterns on tiny wooden chairs. One of her specialties is creating miniature clocks patterned after her husband's vast collection. Wood, jewelry findings, paint and beads go into these clock creations. Patti enjoys _trading_ miniatures with other collectors and artists. Patti and Paul Highfill have been familiar faces at N.A.M.E. Housparties since the club's founding in 1972.

MIRIAM D. IRWIN (MOSAIC PRESS) - "I publish fine miniature books. I do this because I hope eventually to make money. But mainly I publish little books because I believe they will last longer than anything else I could write. When all the advertising paper that our generation has generated has been burned, when all the old magazines and newspapers have been recycled, and all the poorly bound books and paperbooks have become brittle and returned to dust, miniature books will still be carefully kept in top drawer and attic trunk, in library and museum." (For "WHY WRITE A MINIATURE BOOK," by Miriam D. Irwin, send query with SASE to Mosaic Press, 358 Oliver Road, Cincinnati, Ohio 45215. The quotation above, is an excerpt from her fascinating dissertation.)

BARBARA KALTY - "I have been working in miniature scale for about five years and have loved miniatures all my life. I have four kids who keep me busy so I sell very little at present and mainly just enjoy miniatures as 'my thing'. I have a background in jewelry making and use many of those same skills in making miniatures. When my father made Mickey Mouse and Minnie Mouse dresser sets for my children, I copied them to correct 1":1' scale. I also reproduced my baby's crib, even to the workable side of crib which drops on a spring. I design most of my own pieces and I enjoy the challenge of making miniatures that actually 'work', such as turning wheels and clocks that actually tick."

EVELYN DeWOLF NADEL - A widely published journalist listed in "Who's Who of American Women," "Evie" Nadel has been a miniature collector and hobbyist as far back as she can remember. Her first collection, as a child in her native Brazil, was of miniature hand-blown glass animals. At 15, she already was an avid collector of miniature books scaled under 2″; her present collection includes the complete works of Shakespeare, all Moroccan leather-bound, in 1″ editions. A perfectionist by nature, she is both a miniature hobbyist and a collector of the unique works of master miniature craftsmen. As "The Gypsy Merchant," she participates in antiques and collectibles shows, and her pride and joy is her own miniature "operating" antique shop from which she sells her one-of-a-kind mini items. (*See Plate 1*)

Constance E. Stieler - "The winters here are pretty dark and rainy and one cannot read all the time, and I had made many needlepoint pillows and chair seats. So, one day I saw a copy of *Nutshell News*, and was captivated by what I saw and read. We heard about several miniature shops in Seattle and Tacoma and visited them and saw the delightful things they were doing, and loved what we saw. We thought it would be fun to try something like that, so we bought a house kit and had a glorious time building it. I am a frustrated decorator anyway, and I could not believe the things that were available. It opened up a whole new world to us. My husband discovered he enjoyed making little things, so to make a long, long story short, we were hooked. About umpteen hundreds of dollars later, we were surrounded with lathes, drills, saws and you name it; and I bought fabrics, wallpaper and paints. We were off! Yes, off our rockers, some would say! We built a few houses from scratch, of our own design, some from purchased plans, and now we are having fun with room boxes. We think rooms and their furnishings are more visable that way. We search out crafts people and try to have our rooms furnished with original pieces, which cannot always be the case, of course. Some of the better known craft people have priced themselves out of the market for many of us, so it is a joyful experience to discover beautiful things of excellent design and workmanship created by talented people who are unknown but deserve to be recognized. We know we are not skilled experts, but we *are* having fun and find it all worthwhile."

A. THOMAY - "I have been making miniature furniture for seven years. Having spent more than 35 years in the interior design business, I have access to most manufacturer's catalogues. We spent a lot of time researching the miniature market and found a lack of fine quality hand-painted Oriental furniture. Having sold Union National furniture for many years, we decided to produce in miniature some of their line in 1″:1′

scale. Four coats of lacquer are applied to hard wood, (maple and cherry); each coat is sanded and the final coat is sanded with rubbing oil compounded to produce a mirror-like finish. Then the hand-painted *Chinoiserie* decorations are applied. No two pieces are exactly alike, and many hours are required to produce each piece. We estimate that between 75-150 hours go into building the large breakfront and small secretary. Our merchandise is of museum quality and meant for the serious collector. We have been told by knowledgeable experts, that nothing like our merchandise is available world-wide. We offer six standard colors plus two natural wood finishes. We also do custom colors and custom designs for clients. We are glad to answer queries." (See SOURCES)

GEORGIA LUNA VILLALOBOS - "I have always been interested in art. I made dolls for my daughter, Shirley, when she was little. When my two sons, Bill and Mark, and my daughter were grown, I decided to return to school to teach art. At the present time I work for North Orange County, Adult Education Division, Fullerton Community College, California, but I have been teaching for the past ten years. I make all sizes of dolls. Then I began making my own molds for miniature dolls which were first used as decorative lapel pins for doll collectors. But these became so popular, miniature lovers were also asking for them for dollhouses. Now my little dolls are sold throughout the United States, including Hawaii. I make my molds, pour, paint, fire, and repaint. I make the full bodies as well as clothe the dolls. The porcelain is fired 3-4 times before the pieces are joined together. My miniatures have now been selling for four years. I plan to make full-sized original dolls soon , along with original miniature dolls. The Bye-lo "million dollar baby" in miniature, is fashioned after the original. It takes a special sewing machine to produce fitted clothing for the tiny frog-like body. My husband is also an artist, who paints Space scenes."

MARILYN WORTH - (See text accompanying *Plate 8)*

A THUMBNAIL SKETCH ABOUT N.A.M.E.

(National Association of Miniature Enthusiasts, Founded 1972)

Rigid rules governing early manufacture of dollhouses, dictated that they be produced in "period" style. Prefabricated dollhouses imitated life, confining imagination within a closet of modes and manners of the day.

Unquestionably, the historical importance of *period* dollhouses, furniture, and accessories, provide capsular evidence of bygone eras. Meanwhile, the novel and innovative remained off-stage, waiting for the cue of acceptance of new ideas and ideals, and a cunning revolution of the toy industry.

Today's "period" design still provides the needed escape to yesteryear, a nudge of nostalgia, the lulling of disquieting reality. But when imagination lends itself to that reality, it makes even the ordinary artistic. Thus, when ingenuity reached for broader horizons, and imagination stretched to other moons, it was the Space Industry which provided the plastic and adhesive materials for successful new projects, and launched experimentation with quixotic, poetical, and fictive flights of fancy. Fertile minds swept away random cobwebs from the secret corners of Victorian conformity, and the "passion" for miniatures was exposed as something to be unashamedly explored, compared, and shared with others. No longer was the adult miniaturist considered an infantile eccentric; rather one became an *eclectic* eccentric who pondered with child-like wonder the makings of the smallest automation.

It was inevitable that like minds join together for mutual benefit, expression, and understanding; so, under the guidance and experience of the famed miniaturist/collector--the late Allegra Mott--was founded a wanted and needed association whose primary function was "to be the clearing house for miniature collectors and builders"--N.A.M.E.

The National Association of Miniature Enthusiasts is an organization of approximately 12,000 associated members in the United States, Canada, and abroad. Its ideal is the establishment and promotion of educational and philanthropic endeavors in the field of miniatures, and to create, stimulate, and maintain national interest in all matters pertaining to miniatures, both historical and creative.

N.A.M.E. sponsors regional "Houseparties" for the education and enjoyment of its members. These are celebrated annually. At these conventions, miniature exhibits provide a visual education of yesteryear and hints of the future. They also furnish showcases for master craftspeople and for an ever-growing and flourishing "cottage industry" of extremely versatile miniaturists.

From the parent organization come newborn artists who are continually encouraged to develop their full potential in a field represented by one of the most rapid growths in the hobbies and collectibles world.

In a single convention site, superior exhibits of doll-houses are viewed with awe; workshops flint imagination with sparks of creativity and ingenuity; mini-merchandise finds a heady marketplace.

Information about local chapters of N.A.M.E., (chartered by this Association), is reported in the official publication of its quarterly, MINIATURE GAZETTE.

For membership information or replies to queries, send a SASE (self-addressed, stamped envelope) to:

    N.A.M.E.
    P.O. Box 2621, Brookhurst Center
    Anaheim, California 92804-0621
    (Phone: 714-871-NAME)

SOURCES

NAMES & ADDRESSES OF SUPPLIERS WHO
PARTICIPATED IN THIS BOOK

Jenny Biddle,
Cape Cottage Antiques
290 Harbor Drive
Redondo Beach, CA 90277

Cynthia Herrmann
1749 So. Shenandoah St.
Los Angeles, CA 90035

John & Ellen Krucker Blauer
The Miniature Mart
1807 Octavia St.
San Francisco, CA 94109

Patti Highfill
933 Clubhouse Drive
Santa Maria, CA 93455

Barbara Bunce
315 East Second Street
Gaylord, MI 49735

Mosaic Press
(Miriam Irwin)
358 Oliver Road
Cincinnati, OH 45215

Stephanie Blythe and
  Susan Snodgrass
1740 Deep Run Road
Whiteford, MD 21160

Masterpiece Museum Miniatures
(Cecil Boyd)
Box 5280
Austin, TX 78763

Sue Dennis
Pets in Miniature
4317 Lindsay St.
Riverside, CA 92509

The Gypsy Merchant
(Evelyn Nadel)
P.O. Box 2115
Hollywood, CA 90028

Gim Fong
Fong's Gift Shop
939-943 Chungking Rd.
Los Angeles, CA 90012

Jinx Lee Theisen
1959 W. 254 St.
Lomita, CA 90717

Bonnie & Stephen Goode
Many Goode's Catalogue
P.O. Box 5161
Torrance, CA 90510

A. Thomay
Custom Miniatures
599 N.W. 47th Ave.,
Delray Beach, FL 33445

Marilyn Worth Miniature Luthier
554 Coronel Pl. #7
Santa Barbara, CA 93101

ADDITIONAL SOURCES
OF SUPPLY

BOOKS ABOUT MINIATURES
(Old or Out-of-Print)

Collectrix
146 Front St.
Hempstead, NY 11550

Lamplighter Books
Leon, IA 50144

Paul Ruddell
900 Frederick Street
Cumberland, MD 21502

The Reference Rack, Inc.
Box 445C
Orefield, PA 18069

CONTACT: HARD-TO-FIND
MINI-MAKERS or SOURCES

Sarah Salisbury, Columnist
"The Private Eye"
(NUTSHELL NEWS)
P.O. Box 333
Corona del Mar, CA 92625-0333

CUSTOM ORDERS

Gim Fong
939-943 Chungking Rd.
Los Angeles, CA 90012

Bill & Joan Helton
2020 Rodelane
San Diego, CA 92103

Many Goode's
P.O. Box 5161
Torrance, CA 90510

Mox Nix
LaNeva & Glenn Peacock, Owners
3213 17th Street
Metairie, LA 70002

The Gypsy Merchant
P.O. Box 2115
Hollywood, CA 90028

The Miniature Mart
1807 Octavia St.
San Francisco, CA 94109

DOLLHOUSE FIGURES

Stephanie Blythe
1740 Deep Run Road
Whiteford, MD 21160

Patti Highfill
933 Clubhouse Drive
Santa Maria, CA 93455

Sylvia Lyons
2936 Gibbons Dr.
Alameda, CA 94501

Masterpiece Museum Miniatures
Box 5280
Austin, TX 78763

The Miniature Mart
1807 Octavia St.
San Francisco, CA 94109

Georgia L. Villalobos
9352 Steele St.
Rosemead, CA 91770

DOLLHOUSES (Custom/Period)

Robert Lewis Bartlett
40 Caroline St.
Saratoga Springs, NY 12866

Mountain Valley Miniature Shop
Occaquan, VA 22125

Mox Nix
3213 17th Street
Metairie, LA 70002

Southwestern Miniatures
1410 S. Main
Roswell, NM 88201

The Dollhouse Center
Box 706
Montpelier, VT 05602

DOLLHOUSES (Kits)

Lynne's Miniature Treasures
Dept. 24
North Wales, PA 19454

The Dollhouse Center
Box 706
Montepelier, VT 05602

FLOORING (Wood/Scale)

S.H. Goode & Sons Workshop
P.O. Box 5161
Torrance, CA 90510

FURNITURE (Antique/Period)

The Hoffman Collection
P.O. Box 531
Summit, NJ 07901

FURNITURE (Early American)

William Tyson Browne
121 Hillside Ave.
Chatham, NJ 07928

FURNITURE (Eastlake)

The Miniature Mart
1807 Octavia St.
San Francisco, CA 94109

FURNITURE (18th Century)

Roger Gutheil
510 English Rd.
Rochester, NY 14516

FURNITURE (Oriental)

Gim Fong
939-943 Chungking Rd.
Los Angeles, CA 90012

Albert G. Thomay
599 N.W. 47th Ave.
Delray Beach, FL 33445

FURNITURE (Rococo Style)

Nic's Creative Workshop
405 St. Louis Ave.
Point Pleasant Beach, NJ 08742

FURNITURE (Shaker/Penn. Dutch)

The Hoffman Collection
P.O. Box 531
Summit, NJ 07901

FURNITURE (Southwest/Pueblo)

Southwestern Miniatures
1410 S. Main
Roswell, NM 88201

FURNITURE (U.S.A. & Imports)

Willoughby & Taylor Ltd.
2912 Iron Ridge
Dallas, TX 75247

FURNITURE (Victorian)

The Miniature Mart
1807 Octavia St.
San Francisco, CA 94109

GLASS (Blown/molded) MINI

Glass Blowers Workshop
1212 S. Coast Highway
Laguna Beach, CA 92651

MANUFACTURERS & DISTRIBUTORS

Chrysnbon, Heritage in Miniatures,
P.O. Box 13
Western Springs, IL 60558

House of Miniatures
Collectors Society,
Div. of Craftmark,
80 Newbridge Rd.
Bergenfield, NJ 07621

Hummelwerk, Goebel Miniatures &
Company
Dept. M.I.
250 Clearbrook Rd.
Elmsford, NY 10523
(Source: The Butterfly Collection)

Illinois Hobbycraft Inc.
12 S. Fifth Street
Geneva, IL 60134
(Local distributor list for
lighting kits)

Realife Miniatures
Scientific Models, Inc.
340 Snyder Ave.
Berkeley Heights, NJ 07922
(Lists stores carrying kits for
kitchens, bathrooms, etc.)

Reminiscence in Miniature
3206 Old Coach
Camarillo, CA 93010
(Lists shops carrying their complete
line of finished furniture)

The Franklin Mint
Franklin Center, PA 19091
(Cabinet & 1/12″ Scale miniatures in
pewter, porcelain, and other media)

MINI-SCALE LUMBER/MOLDING

S.H. Goode & Sons Workshop
P.O. Box 5161
Torrance, CA 90510

SHOPS (Direct Sale & Query)

Alice's Imagination Shop
2543-B Pacific Coast highway
Torrance, CA 95205

Mostly Miniatures
13759 Ventura Blvd.
Sherman Oaks, CA 91403

MUSICAL ACCESSORIES

The Miniature Mart
1807 Octavia St.
San Francisco, CA 94109

MUSICAL INSTRUMENTS

Marilyn Worth
554 Coronel Pl. #7
Santa Barbara, CA 93101

The Gypsy Merchant
P.O. Box 2115
Hollywood, CA 90028

The Miniature Mart
1807 Octavia St.
San Francisco, CA 94109

MOLDINGS

S.H. Goode & Sons Workshop
P.O. Box 5161
Torrance, CA 90510

ORIENTAL ACCESSORIES

Gim Fong
939-943 Chungking Rd.
Los Angeles, CA 90012

The Furniture Mart
1807 Octavia St.
San Francisco, CA 94109

Oriental Furniture (Custom)

The Heltons
2020 Rodelane
San Diego, CA 92103

Albert G. Thomay
599 N.W. 47th Ave.
Delray Beach, FL 33445

PEWTER

The House of Miniatures
Collectors Society
80 Newbridge Road
Bergenfield, NJ 07621
(Williamsburg Reproductions)

PICTURE FRAME MOLDING

S.H. Goode & Sons Workshop
P.O. Box 5161
Torrance, CA 90510

PICTURE FRAMES (Assorted)

The Miniature Mart
1807 Octavia St.
San Francisco, CA 94109

TOOLS & ACCESSORIES
(Mini-work)

S.H. Goode & Sons Workshop
P.O. Box 5161
Torrance, CA 90510

VARIETY 1/12 SCALE
MINIATURES

The Miniature Catalog
Boynton and Associates, Inc.
Clifton House,
Clifton, VA 22024

WALLPAPER (Scale & Specialty)

The Miniature Mart
1807 Octavia St.
San Francisco, CA 94109

WORKSHOP EQUIP. (1/12 scale)

Many Goode's Catalogue
P.O. Box 5161
Torrance, CA 90510

Note: The SOURCES given are primarily for the benefit of mini-makers & collectors who DO NOT have access to local miniature shops and/or for those who are unable to find a specific item at their local hobby or miniature haven. When writing for information to any SOURCE, please enclose a SELF ADDRESSED STAMPED ENVELOPE to assure: 1) a reply; 2)that your address is correct.

SASE=self-addressed stamped envelope. A #10 (business-size) envelope is best when sending for information.

Many SOURCES are happy to answer telephone queries. Their phone numbers are listed in local directories. Because some SOURCES have specific business hours, it's always a good idea to check BY TELEPHONE to avoid disappointment, time, energy, and fuel.

Hundreds of other sources can be found in the newsletters, periodicals, and reference books listed in this book. New sources are always cropping up. To keep on top of the miniature field, the author suggests readership of one or more periodicals on the subject of miniatures, as well as membership in either a local or national organization devoted to the furtherance of miniature hobbying.

NEWSLETTERS, PERIODICALS & TRADE PUBLICATIONS

Antique Collectors' Club
9 E. Savannah Park
Ithaca, NY 14850

Antique Toy World
3941 Belle Plaine Ave.
Chicago, IL 60618

Doll Reader
Hobby House Press, Inc.
900 Frederick St.
Cumberland, MD 21502

Doll Castle News
P.O. Box 247
Washington, NJ 07882

Hobbies
Lightner Publishing Co.
1006 S. Michigan Ave.
Chicago, IL 60605

Int'l Dolls' House News
56 Lincoln Wood
Haywards Heath RH16 1LH
Sussex, England

Miniature Collector
Acquire Publishing Co.
170 Fifth Ave.
New York, NY 10010

Miniature Gazette
N.A.M.E.
P.O. Box 2621
Brookhurst Center
Anaheim, CA 92804

Miniature Makers Journal
409 South First St.
Evansville, WI 53536

Miniature Reflections
409 South First St.
Evansville, WI 53536

Mott's Miniature Workshop News
P.O. Box 5514
Sunny Hills Station
Fullerton, CA 92635

Nutshell News
Clifton House
Clifton, VA 22024

Small Talk
P.O. Box 334
Laguna Beach, CA 92651

The Teddy Bear & Friends
Hobby House Press, Inc.
900 Frederick St.
Cumberland, MD 21502

The Antique Trader Weekly
Annual of Articles
P.O. Box 1050
Dubuque, IA 52001

Theriault's
P.O. Box 151
Annapolis, MD 21404

The Berry Hill News
Canyon Route,
Gallatin Gateway,
Billings, MT 59730

The Doll House and Miniature News
3 Orchard Lane
Kirkwood, MO 63122

The Miniature Magazine
Carstens Publications, Inc.
P.O. Box 700
Newton, NJ 07860

The Scale Cabinetmaker: A Journal for Miniaturist
Dorsett Miniatures
P.O. Box 87
Pembroke, VA 24136

Victorian Homes
P.O. Box 61
Millers Falls, MA 01349

Yankee Magazine
Yankee, Inc.
Dublin, NH 03444

CATALOGUES

Many advertisers listed in the NEWSLETTERS, PERIODICALS, and TRADE PUBLICATIONS section, offer diversified catalogs. Prices for catalogs vary; some are offered FREE; others that cost $2.00 or more, will credit the amount on a first purchase. To receive information regarding catalogs, send SASE attention: ORDER DEPT.

The sources listed below, represent those mentioned in this book WHO DO HAVE catalogs offering mini-merchandise.

Lynne's Miniature Treasures
Dept. 24,
North Wales, PA 19454

The House of Miniatures
80 Newbridge Road
Bergenfield, NJ 07621

Many Goode's Catalogue
P.O. Box 5161
Torrance, CA 90510

The Miniature Mart
1807 Octavia St.
San Francisco, CA 94109

Masterpiece Museum
Miniatures
Box 5280
Austin, TX 78763

Theriault's,
"Miniatures at Auction"
P.O. Box 151
Annapolis, MD 21404

Mosaic Press
358 Oliver Road
Cincinnati, OH 45215

Washington Dolls' House
& Toy Museum
5236 44th St., NW
Washington, DC 20015

Mott's Miniatures
P.O. Box 5514
Sunny Hills Stations
Fullerton, CA 92635

Yankee Notions
52790 Brooktrails
South Bend, IN 46637

S.H. Goode & Sons
"The Scale Cabinetmaker"
Dorsett Publications
P.O. Box 5161
Torrance, CA 90510

Wee Wonders
222 7th Street
Seal Beach, CA 90740

Smithsonian Institution
P.O. Box 2456
Washington, DC 20013

Willoughby & Taylor Ltd.
International Merchants
2912 Iron Ridge
Dallas, TX 75247

SUGGESTED BOOKS FOR ADDITIONAL READING AND REFERENCE

Few books on this Reference List have been published in this decade. Many are reprints of earlier works or were available as First Editions in the late sixties and mid-seventies. All are worthwhile, informative, and enlightening. Much that's *new* in the quest of reducing everything to its smallest denomination, entered this fascinating field of make-believe through space technology, experimentation in plastics and adhesives, and computerized reduction processes. Sophisticated electrification has brightened the prospects of superior lighting devices for miniature mansions and dollhouses. Interest in scaled miniatures to match the HO "railroadmania", is the newest engrossing trend for mini-makers. (See NEWSLETTERS, PERIODICALS & TRADE PUBLICATIONS section of this book for current information about these newest innovations.)

Benson, Arthur - *Everybody's Book of the Queen's Doll House*, The Daily Telegraph and Metheun & Co., London (1924).

_____, and Lawrence Weaver - *The Book of the Queen's Doll House*, Metheun & Co., London (1924).

Bishop, Robert and Patricia Coblentz - *The World of Antiques, Art, and Architecture in Victorian America*, E.P. Dutton, NY (1979).

Brann, Donald - *How to Build Dollhouses and Furniture*, Briarcliff Manor, (1976). (Simple directions)

Buser, M. Elaine and Dan - *Schoenhut's Dolls, Toys and Circus (1872-1967)*, Collector Books, Paducah, KY (1976).

Cadbury, Betty - *Playthings Past*, Praeger Publishers, Inc., New York, NY (1976).

Cole, Christopher - *Make Your Own Doll House*, Van Nostrand Reinhold, (1976).

Coleman, Dorothy S., Elizabeth A. and Evelyn J., *The Collector's Book of Doll's Clothes*, Crown Publishers, Inc., NY (1975).

Consumer Guide, (Editors) - *Miniatures*, Beekman House, NY (1979).

Cummings, Richard - *Make Your Own Dollhouses*, David McKay, New York, (1978).

Desmonde, Kay - *Dolls and Dolls Houses*, The World Publishing Co., New York (1972).

Dorsett, Helen - *Cabinetmaker's Guide for Doll House Furniture*, Doll Books, 4701 Queensburg Rd., Riverdale, MD (1964).

Duda, Margaret B. - *Miniature Shops: How to Design and Make Them*, A.S. Barnes, South Brunswick, NJ (1975).

Farlie, Barbara L. with Charlotte L. Clarke - *All About Doll Houses*, Bobbs-Merrill Co., Inc., Indianapolis/New York (1975).

Fish, Helen Dean - *The Doll House Book*, Stokes, NY (19410).

Foskett, Daphne - *Collecting Miniatures*, Antique Collectors, 9 East Savannah, Ithaca, NY 14850, (1980).

Goode, Stephen - *Introduction to Woods for Miniature Model Making*, P.O. Box 5161, Torrance, CA 90510, (1980). (Includes wood samples)

Helberg, Kristin - *Art Deco, Doll House Book*, Rainy Day Press, Berkeley, CA.

_____ - *Victorian Doll House Book*, Rainy Day Press, Berkeley, California.

Hobby House Press - *Victoriana Dollhouse: 1876*, Hobby House, Riverdale, Maryland.

Houart, Colonel Victor - *Miniature Silver Toys*, Alpine Fine Arts Collection, Ltd., 164 Madison Ave., NY 10016 (1983).

Jacobs, Flora Gill - *A History of Doll's Houses*, Scribner's, (1953); Cassell, England, (1954).

_____ - *A World of Doll Houses*, Gramercy Publishing Co., New York, NY.

_____ - *Doll's Houses in America: Historic Preservation in Miniature*, Charles Scribner's Sons, New York (1974).

_____ - and Estrid Faurholt - *A Book of Dolls and Doll Houses*, Charles E. Tuttle, Vermont, (1967).

Jellison, Phyllis - *The Colonial Dollhouse*, Van Nostrand Reinhold, (1977).

Johnson, Audrey - *Furnishing Doll Houses*, C.T. Branford, Newton Centre, MA (1972).

_____ - *How to Make Dolls' Houses*, Wm. Clowes & Sons Ltd., London, (1957).

Kelly, Karin - *Doll's Houses*, Lerner Pub., Minneapolis, (1974).

Ketchum, Wm. C., Jr. - *Toys and Games*, The Smithsonian Institution's National Museum of Design, (1981).

Latham, Jean - *Collecting Miniature Antiques* Charles Scribner's Sons, New York, (1972).

_____ - *Dolls' Houses: A Personal Choice*, Charles Scribner's Sons, New York, (1969).

Lechler, Doris & Virginia O'Neill - *A Collector's Guide to Children's Glass Dishes*, Thomas Nelson, Inc. Publishers, Nashville, Tenn., (1976).

Lee, Tina - *How to Make Doll's Houses*, Doubleday, NY (1948).

MacLaren, Catherine B. - *This Side of Yesterday in Miniature*, Nutshell News, 1035 Newkirk Drive, La Jolla, CA 92037, (1975). (Contains excellent list of SOURCES & DECORATOR GUIDE)

McClinton, Katharine Morrison - *Antiques in Miniature*, Charles Scribner's Sons, New York, (1970).

_____ - *Antiques of American Childhood*, Clarkson N. Potter, Inc., NY (1970).

_____ - *The Complete Book of Small Antiques Collecting*, Bramhall House, Div. Clarkson N. Potter, Inc., NY (1965).

McElroy, Joan - *Joan McElroy's Doll House Furniture Book*, Random House, NY, (1976).

Mackay, James - *An Encyclopedia of Small Antiques*, Harper & Row, Publishers, New York, (1975).

Manos, Susan - *Schoenhut Dolls & Toys*, Collector Books, Paducah, Ky, (1971).

Meras, Phyllis - *Miniatures*, Houghton Mifflin Co., Boston, (1976).

Merrill, Virginia & Jean Jessop - *Needlework in Miniature*, Crown Publishers, Inc., New York, (1978).

Meyer, Barbara - *Meyer's Homemade Meals*, Boynton & Assoc., Inc., 12 Clifton House, Clifton, VA, (1983).

Mitchell, Donald E. & Helene A. - *Dollhouses Past & Present*, Collector Books, Paducah, KY (1980)

Moore, Colleen - *Colleen Moore's Doll House*, Doubleday, Garden City, NY, (1971).

Moreland, F.A. - *The Curtain-maker's Handbook*, (originally published, 1889); reprinted by E.P. Dutton, NY, (1979).

Musgrave, Clifford - *Queen Mary's Dolls' House and Dolls Belonging to H.M. the Queen*, Garrod & Lofthouse International, Ltd., London, (1970).

Newman, Thelma & Virginia Merrill - *The Complete Book of Making Miniatures - (For Room Settings & Dollhouses)*, Crown Publishers, Inc., New York, (1975). (Excellent sources of supply)

Noble, John - *A Fabulous Dollhouse of the Twenties*, Dover, NY (1976).

O'Brien, Marian Maeve - *Make Your Own Doll Houses and Dollhouse Miniatures*, Hawthorne Books, NY, (1975).

O'Brien, Richard - *Collecting Toys*, Books Americana, Inc., Florence, Alabama, (1979).

Pipe, Ann Kimball - *Reproducing Furniture in Miniature*, Henry Regnery, Chicago, (1976).

Roche, P.K. - *Dollhouse Magic: How to Make and Find Simple Dollhouse Furniture*, Dial, NY, (1977).

Ruthberg, Helen - *Miniature Room Settings*, Chilton Book Co., Radnor, Pa., (1978).

_____ - *The Book of Miniatures: Furniture and Accessories*, Chilton, Philadelphia, (1977). (Excellent "How To" & Source Supply)

Schiffer, Peter B., & Herbert F. - *Miniature Antique Furniture*, Livingston Publishing Co., Wynnewood, Pa., (1976).

Schroeder, Joseph J., Jr. - *The Wonderful World of Toys, Games & Dolls (1860-1930)*, Follett Publishing Co., Chicago (1971).
Smith, Harry W. - *The Art of Making Furniture in Miniature*, Dutton, New York, (1983).
Spinning Wheel's - *Complete Book of Dolls*, edited by Albert Christian Revi, Galahad Books, NY, (1975).
Thorne, Mrs. James Ward - *American Rooms in Miniature*, The Art Institute, Chicago, (1962).
_____ - European Rooms in Miniature, The Art Institute, Chicago, (1962).
Time-Life Books - *The Encyclopedia of Collectibles*, Chicago, (1980). (Book Series - "Toys")
Weltens, Arno - *Mechanical Tin Toys in Color*, Sterling Publishing Co., Inc., (1979).
Whitney, Marylou - *Cornelia Vanderbilt Whitney's Dollhouse: The Story of a Dollhouse and the People Who Lived In It*, Farrar, Straus & Giroux, NY, (1975).
Whitton, Blair - *Bliss Toys & Dollhouses*, Dover Publications, Inc., with The Margaret Woodbury Strong Museum, (1979).
Williams, Guy R. - *Making a Miniature House* Oxford University Press, Oxford, (1964).
Worrell, Estelle Ansley - *Americana in Miniature*, Van Nostrand Reinhold Company, NY, (1973).
_____ - *The Dollhouse Book*, Van Nostrand Co., Inc., (1966).

FOR OUT-OF-PRINT OR HARD-TO-FIND TITLES

Collectrix, 146 Front St., Hempstead, NY 11550.
Lamplighter Books, Leon, IA 50144.
Paul Ruddell, 4701 N. Queensbury Rd., Riverdale, MD 20840.*
The Reference Rack, Box 445C, Orefield, PA 18069.

(*A major source for books about miniatures)

VALUE GUIDE

The majority of the items listed are pictured in this book. Some miniatures shown are one-of-a-kind, and NOT FOR SALE. Others were gifts to the author. In the latter case, similar pieces have been found in various catalogues, and those are the values listed, and serve merely as *guides* for the collector. Values are rounded to *even* dollars.

Although only one source per item is listed in this VALUE GUIDE, the source was either the actual supplier to the author, or has proven to be a current marketplace for the collector. However, simply because a source is listed in this guide, it does not necessarily infer that it is the *primary* source.

ITEM	SOURCE	VALUE
Apple barrel (ass't apples)	Many Goode's Catalogue	6.00
Baby, 1½″ all-bisque	Many Goode's Catalogue	16.00
Baby, Christening outfit	Patti Highfill	30.00
Baby Layette Set	Patti Highfill	35.00
Baby's Afghan, 1¾″x2″	Many Goode's Catalogue	10.00
Baby's bonnet & booties	Many Goode's Catalogue	7.00
Baked cakes, pies, cookies, etc.	Many Goode's Catalogue	2.00-4.00
Baked specialties/Gourmet foods & delicacies	The Miniature Mart	8.00-15.00
Barrels (wood)ass't sizes	Many Goode's Catalogue	1.00-2.00
Basket w/eggs	Many Goode's Catalogue	3.00
Basket w/green or red apples	Many Goode's Catalogue	3.00
Bassinette, (crochet covered)	Many Goode's Catalogue	20.00
Bathroom fixtures (porcelain)	Lynne's Mini. Treasures	13.00-23.00
Bedwarmer, 3″ brass plated	Lynne's Mini. Treasures	3.00
Bell, 1″ cobalt, blown by Mary Szalczer	Lynne's Mini. Treasures	6.00
Bench, Park (4¼″x2½″) metal	Lynne's Mini. Treasures	2.00
Bird Cages, Plain/fancy	The Miniature Mart	15.00-100.00
Blue Spatterware utensils (priced per set)	Many Goode's Catalogue	2.00-3.00 20.00-25.00
Books, tooled leather	Mosaic Press	75.00
Brass Spittoon, ½″	Many Goode's Catalogue	2.00
Bread in loaf pan	Many Goode's Catalogue	2.00
Bride & Groom (china w/dome	Alice's Imagination Shop	7.00

ITEM	SOURCE	VALUE
Busts, figurines, statues	The Miniature Mart	7.00-9.00
"Butterfly Collection" Furniture (Goebel)	The Miniature Mart	18.00-48.00
"Butterfly Collection" Case	The Miniature Mart	60.00
Buttons on cards	Many Goode's Catalogue	2.00/3.00
Cake, (3-tier wedding), John M. Blauer, original	The Miniature Mart	12.00
Candy Jar, 1" w/cork	Many Goode's Catalogue	2.00
Cans (juice w/labels) Set of 3	Lynne's Mini. Treasures	2.00
Cat (Vienna Bronze)	Cape Cottage Antiques	55.00-75.00
Cats (various breeds)	Sue Dennis	23.00
Cats (Kittens in Basket), Limited Edition	Sue Dennis	35.00
Chandeliers (variety), including gold plated	The Miniature Mart	65.00-350.00
Christmas 3/8" candy canes pkg/6	Many Goode's Catalogue	.75
Christmas Centerpiece w/glass chimney, candle, pinecones	Many Goode's Catalogue	10.00
Christmas garland, (20") red, green, gold, silver "tinsel" (Priced each)	Many Goode's Catalogue	.75
Christmas gift-wrapped pkg.	Cynthia Herrmann	2.00-4.00
Christmas Gingerbread House 7/16"x3/4"x1"	Many Goode's Catalogue	10.00
Christmas Ornaments, see-thru box (9 in box)	Many Goode's Catalogue	4.00
Christmas Ornaments (½" scale) Priced per set	Many Goode's Catalogue	10.00
Christmas Plates (Special Editions, Ellen Krucker Blauer)	The Miniature Mart	7.00
Christmas Poinsettia in pot	Many Goode's Catalogue	10.00
Christmas Shopping bag w/toys	Many Goode's Catalogue	1.00
Christmas Stocking (crochet)	Many Goode's Catalogue	7.00
Christmas Tree (Lycopodium, 6" or 8")	Many Goode's Catalogue	15.00
Christmas Tree Ornaments, incl. tinsel, garland, canes, etc. (Priced per set)	Many Goode's Catalogue	15.00
Christmas Tree Top Angel	Many Goode's Catalogue	2.00
Christmas Wrapping Paper, 3 sheets, ea. 5½"x8½"	Many Goode's Catalogue	.80

ITEM	SOURCE	VALUE
Clocks (Mantle)	Patti Highfill	10.00-30.00
Clocks (Wall/Victorian)	The Miniature Mart	44.00
Clothes (Baby's dress, bib, rompers, sunsuit, etc.)	Patti Highfill	25.00-35.00
Cookies w/glass of milk	Many Goode's Catalogue	4.00
Corsage	Many Goode's Catalogue	3.00
Coverlets (handwoven orig.)	The Miniature Mart	35.00
Cracker barrel (filled)	Many Goode's Catalogue	6.00
Crates (wood) w/produce, in ass't sizes	Many Goode's Catalogue	4.00-6.00
Crochet thread mini-ball ¼". (Priced each)	Many Goode's Catalogue	.75
Crochet doilies (single or sofa sets, etc.)	Many Goode's Catalogue	3.00-15.00
Dinnerware (El Kru® ass't) (Priced each)	The Miniature Mart	8.00-16.00
Dogs (various breeds)	Sue Dennis	23.00
Dome (glass)	Alice's Imagination Shop	2.00-5.00
Dresser Set (15/pc. vanity handpainted)	The Miniature Mart	20.00
Dress form (black metal)	Many Goode's Catalogue	2.00
Eastlake dining room furniture, ca. 1868	The Miniature Mart	23.00-50.00
El Kru® Dinnerware	The Miniature Mart	8.00-16.00
Fireplace accessories	The Miniature Mart	18.00-45.00
Fireplace mantles (Victorian)	The Miniature Mart	18.00-25.00
Flour Sack ("50 lbs.")	Many Goode's Catalogue	.75
Food, gourmet platters of party & holiday treats, Linda Warter, artist	The Miniature Mart	8.00-13.00
Fruit (assorted)	Many Goode's Catalogue	.30-.75
Foods (assorted)	Many Goode's Catalogue	2.00-7.00
Fruit (boxed)	Many Goode's Catalogue	3.00-4.00
Fruits & Vegetables (4 crates filled)	Many Goode's Catalogue	48.00
Games, ass't (pool, monopoly, parcheesi, chess, etc.)	The Miniature Mart	80.00-250.00
Gift-wrapped packages	Cynthia Herrmann	2.00-4.00
Glass w/iced tea, lemonade, milk	Many Goode's Catalogue	2.00
Glass-blown jars w/wired lid	Alice's Imagination Shop	3.00
Globe Stand (Victorian)	The Miniature Mart	175.00

ITEM	SOURCE	VALUE
Goebel Miniatures & Co. ("Butterfly Collection") *The Stuart Library*	The Miniature Mart	
Queen Anne Secretary		48.00
Wm. & Mary Side Table		36.00
Wm. & Mary Tall Case Clock		48.00
Baroque Frame		10.00
Wm. & Mary Wing Chair		36.00
Wm. & Mary Side Chair		18.00
Queen Anne Bookcase		48.00
Charles II Armchair		18.00
Stuart Libr. Display Case		64.00
Goldfish in bowl	Lynne's Mini. Treasures	8.00
Groceries (½", w/country store old-time labels)	Lynne's Mini Treasures	4.00/24.00
Hat or Wig Stands	Many Goode's Catalogue	3.00
Household Wares	Many Goode's Catalogue	.50-6.00
Ivory Thimble	Many Goode's Catalogue	4.00
Jar (glass, for canning)	Alice's Imagination	3.00-4.00
Jewelry (scale 1"-1' size)	Barbara Bunce	12.00-26.00
Kerosene Stove (cast metal)	Lynne's Mini. Treasures	3.00
Kitchen Wares	Many Goode's Catalogue	1.00-3.00
Lamps (hanging/parlor)	The Miniature Mart	64.00
Material (4 bolts/fabric) (Priced per set)	Many Goode's Catalogue	2.00
Metallic Dog w/shoe	Alice's Imagination Shop	8.00-10.00
Morton's Salt Box ½"	Lynne's Mini. Treasures	2.00
Packages, gift-wrapped	Cynthia Herrmann	2.00-4.00
Patterns (sewing)	Many Goode's Catalogue	2.00
Pedestals	The Miniature Mart	8.00-18.00
Pets (dogs & cats)	Sue Dennis	23.00
Picture Frames (ass't, brass, gilded)	The Miniature Mart	2.00-3.00
Picture Frames (composition)	The Miniature Mart	6.00-9.00
Pincushion ("tomato")	Many Goode's Catalogue	2.00
Pitcher, iced tea, milk, ade	Many Goode's Catalogue	3.00
Plants (ass't) & Flowers	The Miniature Mart	8.00-16.00
Porcelain Dolls (mini-size)	Stephanie Blythe	75.00
Porcelain Baby (dressed)	Patti Highfill	30.00
Porcelain "Bye-Lo Baby" (dressed)	Georgia Luna Villalobos	60.00

ITEM	SOURCE	VALUE
Pram (old-fashioned carriage)	Lynne's Mini.Treasures	4.00
Produce Crates (wood)	Many Goode's Catalogue	2.00
Produce Stand w/4 paper-labelled crates (unfilled)	Many Goode's Catalogue	12.00
Raggedy Ann & Andy	Wee Wonders Miniatures	3.00
"Ribbon", 3 rolls/tiny spool	Many Goode's Catalogue	1.00
Rolling Pin (maple wood)	Many Goode's Catalogue	2.00
Safety Pin	Many Goode's Catalogue	.60
Scissors, 1″ metal	Many Goode's Catalogue	.50
Shawl (crochet)	Many Goode's Catalogue	12.00
Sheet Music (asst'd)	The Miniature Mart	3.00/4.00
Shelves (unfinished Alder wood, for old-fashioned mdse.)	Many Goode's Catalogue	6.00-7.00
Slippers (bedroom)	Many Goode's Catalogue	5.00
Sock Darner (Boxwood)	Many Goode's Catalogue	4.00
Spittoon, ½″ brass	Many Goode's Catalogue	2.00
Sterling Silver Furniture ½″ scale. German	Cape Cottage Antiques	350.00-1200.00
Table Accessories (gold/silver) (Sterling by Guglielmo Cini)	The Miniature Mart	8.00-86.00
Tables (accessory)	The Miniature Mart	40.00-80.00
Threads .08″ dia. x 1/8″ Boxwood, spools ass't colors (Priced each)	Many Goode's Catalogue	2.00
Towel Rack (Victorian)	The Miniature Mart	40.00
Trays (enamelled brass)	The Miniature Mart	10.00
Tub, (metal) w/beer, soda on ice	Many Goode's Catalogue	7.00
Vanity Set (15/pc. UNPAINTED, plastic ½″ to 1″ pcs.)	Lynne's Mini. Treasures	6.00
Vegetables, assorted, ea.	Many Goode's Catalogue	1.00-2.00
Vegetables (boxed), ea.	Many Goode's Catalogue	3.00
Victorian Wall Clock	Alice's Imagination Shop	36.00
Vienna Bronze Dog on cushion	Cape Cottage Antiques	65.00-85.00
Violin (one-of-a-kind) w/bow	Marilyn Worth Studio	400.00
Wallpaper (Special Design)	The Miniature Mart	1.00-3.00
Wig Stand	Many Goode's Catalogue	3.00
Wine Glass (art glass)	Alice's Imagination Shop	45.00-65.00
Wrapping Paper (Two 3/roll pkgs.)	Many Goode's Catalogue	4.00

Other Books by Lillian Baker

Hatpins and Hatpin Holders $9.95
5½x8½, 160 pages, paperback
ISBN: 0-89145-224-9

Art Nouveau & Art Deco Jewelry $9.95
5½x8½, 176 pages, paperback
ISBN: 0-89145-158-7

100 Years of Collectible Jewelry $9.95
5½x8½, 169 pages, paperback
ISBN: 0-89145-066-1

Available from your favorite bookseller or from:

Collector Books
P.O. Box 3009
Paducah, Kentucky 42001

or

Lillian Baker
15237 Chanera Ave.
Alondra Park,
Gardena, California 90249

Please add $1.00 for shipping and handling when ordering by mail.